Limited com[pany]
accounts

Workbook

1.6

David Cox

osborne
BOOKS

Published by Osborne Books Limited
Unit 1B Everoak Estate
Bromyard Road
Worcester WR2 5HP
Tel 01905 748071
Email books@osbornebooks.co.uk
Website www.osbornebooks.co.uk

Design by Laura Ingham
Cover and page design image © Istockphoto.com/Petrovich9

Printed by CPI Antony Rowe, Chippenham and Eastbourne

British Library Cataloguing in Publication Data
A catalogue record for this book is available from the British Library

ISBN 978 1905777 501

Contents

Chapter activities

Chapter activities – answers

Practice assessments

Practice assessments – answers

Acknowledgements

The author wishes to thank the following for their help with the production of the book: Jean Cox, Maz Loton, Jon Moore and Cathy Turner. Thanks are also due to Roger Petheram for his technical editing and to Laura Ingham for her designs for this new series.

The publisher is indebted to the Association of Accounting Technicians for its kind permission to reproduce sample practice assessment material.

Author

David Cox is a Certified Accountant with more than twenty years' experience teaching accountancy students over a wide range of levels. Formerly with the Management and Professional Studies Department at Worcester College of Technology, he now lectures on a freelance basis and carries out educational consultancy work in accountancy studies. He is author and joint author of a number of textbooks in the areas of accounting, finance and banking.

Introduction

what this book covers

This book has been written specifically to cover the Learning Area 'Financial Statements' which combines two QCF Units in the AAT Level 4 Diploma in Accounting:

- Principles of drafting financial statements
- Drafting financial statements

what this book contains

This book is set out in two sections:

- **Chapter activities** which provide extra practice material in addition to the activities included in the Osborne Books Tutorial text. Answers to the Chapter activities are set out in this book.
- **Practice Assessments** are included to prepare the student for the Computer Based Assessments. They are based directly on the structure, style and content of the sample assessment material provided by the AAT at www.aat.org.uk. Suggested answers to the Practice Assessments are set out in this book.

online support from Osborne Books

This book is supported by practice material available at www.osbornebooks.co.uk

This material is available to tutors – and to students at their discretion – in two forms:

- A **Tutor Zone** which is available to tutors who have adopted the Osborne Books texts. This area of the website provides extra assessment practice material (plus answers) in addition to the activities included in this Workbook text.
- **E-learning** – online practice questions designed to familiarise students with the style of the AAT Computer Based Assessments.

further information

If you want to know more about our products, please visit www.osbornebooks.co.uk, email books@osbornebooks.co.uk or telephone Osborne Books Customer Services on 01905 748071.

Chapter activities

Chapter activities

1

Purpose of financial statements

1.1 (a) What is the objective of financial statements according to the *Framework for the Preparation and Presentation of Financial Statements*?

 (b) Give TWO examples of types of external users of financial statements. For each user, identify their purpose in using information in financial statements.

1.2 Which one of the following statements is correct?

	✔
income − expenses = profits or losses	
assets − expenses = profits or losses	
assets + expenses = profits or losses	
income + expenses = profits or losses	

1.3 Which one of the following options is correct?

Assets £	Liabilities £	Equity £	✔
20,600	8,350	28,950	
16,850	7,950	7,900	
18,550	8,200	10,530	
35,250	14,600	20,650	

1.4 The *Framework for the Preparation and Presentation of Financial Statements* identifies four principal qualitative characteristics that make the information provided in financial statements useful to users.

Write in the characteristic that relates to each of the statements below.

Statement	Characteristic
Financial information that is useful to users of the financial statements	
Financial information that can be depended upon by users	
Financial statements that can be compared with those from previous years	
Users of financial statements can understand the information given	

1.5 (a) Set out the accounting equation and define the elements in the equation.

(b) Briefly explain how profit for the year affects the elements of the accounting equation.

1.6 (a) What are the elements that appear in financial statements according to the *Framework for the Preparation and Presentation of Financial Statements*?

(b) Define the elements that appear in the statement of comprehensive income in accordance with the definitions in the *Framework for the Preparation and Presentation of Financial Statements*.

Chapter activities

2 Introduction to limited company financial statements

A layout for a statement of comprehensive income and a statement of financial position is included in the Appendix of *Limited company accounts tutorial*, and is also available in the Resources section of www.osbornebooks.co.uk.

2.1 (a) Define a public limited company (plc)

(b) Define a private limited company (ltd)

2.2 What is meant by a limited company having a separate legal entity?

	✔
the name of the company is different from that of the individual shareholders	
anyone taking legal action proceeds against the company and not the individual shareholders	
in the event of the company becoming insolvent, the shareholders can only lose the amount of their investment	
the directors manage the company on behalf of shareholders	

2.3 Which one of the following investments in a company usually carries voting rights at meetings of the company?

	✔
ordinary shares	
preference shares	
debentures	
long-term loans	

2.4 A new company issues 100,000 ordinary shares of 50p each at a premium of 10 per cent. What amount will be shown as the total of the equity section of the company's statement of financial position?

	✔
£100,000	
£110,000	
£50,000	
£55,000	

2.5 Crantock plc prepares its financial statements to 31 March each year. At 31 March 20-2 its trial balance was as follows:

	£000	£000
Administrative expenses	240	
Share capital		700
Trade and other receivables	525	
Cash and cash equivalents	75	
Share premium		200
Distribution costs	500	
Plant and equipment at cost	1,600	
Accumulated depreciation on plant and equipment		500
Retained earnings at 1 April 20-1		350
Purchases	1,200	
Inventories at 1 April 20-1	160	
Trade and other payables		395
Sales		2,295
Dividends paid	140	
	4,440	4,440

Additional information

- Inventories at 31 March 20-2 cost £180,000.

- The corporation tax charge for the year has been calculated as £65,000.

- Depreciation on plant and equipment has already been provided for in the list of balances above and allocated to distribution costs and administrative expenses accordingly.

REQUIRED

Prepare the financial statements of Crantock plc for the year ended 31 March 20-2.

2.6 Playfair Ltd prepares its financial statements to 31 December each year. At 31 December 20-3 its trial balance was as follows:

	£000	£000
Share capital		580
Share premium		50
Land at cost	500	
Plant and equipment at cost	800	
Trade receivables	350	
Trade payables		160
Accruals		30
Prepayments	40	
Cash and cash equivalents	140	
Long-term loan		200
Inventories at 1 January 20-3	250	
Administrative expenses	110	
Purchases	1,650	
Sales		2,340
Debenture interest paid	20	
Distribution costs	240	
Accumulated depreciation on plant and equipment		230
Dividends paid	50	
Retained earnings at 1 January 20-3		540
Provision for doubtful receivables at 1 January 20-3		20
	4,150	4,150

Additional information

- Inventories at 31 December 20-3 cost £280,000

- Depreciation of plant and equipment is to be charged at the rate of 20 per cent per annum on cost and allocated equally between distribution costs and administrative expenses

- The provision for doubtful receivables is to be increased to £40,000

- Interest on the long-term loan has not been paid for the second half of the year; the interest due amounts to £20,000

- The corporation tax charge for the year has been calculated as £30,000

REQUIRED

Prepare the financial statements of Playfair Ltd for the year to 31 December 20-3.

Chapter activities

3

Published financial statements of limited companies

A layout for a statement of comprehensive income and a statement of financial position is included in the Appendix of *Limited company accounts tutorial*, and is also available in the Resources section of www.osbornebooks.co.uk.

3.1 Complete the following sentence taken from IAS 1, *Presentation of Financial Statements*:

'The objective of financial statements is to provide .... about the

.... position, financial .... and ....

flows of an entity that is .... to a wide range of .... in

making .... decisions.'

Choose from the following words:

cash

economic

financial

information

performance

useful

users

3.2 According to IAS 1, *Presentation of Financial Statements*, which of the following is included in a complete set of financial statements?

1.   statement of comprehensive income
2.   statement of cash flows
3.   directors' report
4.   statement of changes in equity

	✔
1 and 2	
1, 2 and 3	
1, 2 and 4	
all of them	

3.3 What are the deadlines for filing the statutory accounts with the Registrar of Companies for (i) a private limited company and (ii) a public limited company?

		✔
(i) nine months	(ii) nine months	
(i) six months	(ii) six months	
(i) six months	(ii) nine months	
(i) nine months	(ii) six months	

3.4 Which of the following is included under the heading for 'Equity' in a statement of financial position?

1. revaluation reserve
2. bank loans
3. share premium
4. long-term provisions

	✔
1 and 2	
1, 2 and 3	
1 and 3	
all of them	

3.5 Which of the following involves a cash flow?

1. a rights issue of shares
2. the revaluation of a non-current asset
3. depreciation of non-current assets
4. a bonus issue of shares

	✔
1	
1 and 2	
1, 2 and 3	
all of them	

3.6 According to IAS 8, *Accounting Policies, Changes in Accounting Estimates and Errors*, how are accounting policies defined? Give one example of an accounting policy that might be used by a limited company.

3.7 The Chief Accountant of Quine Limited has asked you to help prepare the financial statements for the year ended 30 September 20-4. The trial balance of the company as at 30 September 20-4 is set out below.

Quine Limited
Trial balance as at 30 September 20-4

	Debit	Credit
	£000	£000
Share capital		3,000
Interest paid	200	
Trade and other receivables	1,802	
Dividends paid	600	
Long-term loan		2,500
Distribution costs	980	
Administrative expenses	461	
Sales		10,884
Retained earnings at 1 October 20-3		1,457
Cash and cash equivalents	103	
Accruals		105
Prepayments	84	
Share premium		500
Land – cost	3,600	
Buildings – cost	1,480	
Fixtures and fittings – cost	645	
Vehicles – cost	1,632	
Office equipment – cost	447	
Buildings – accumulated depreciation		702
Fixtures and fittings – accumulated depreciation		317
Vehicles – accumulated depreciation		903
Office equipment – accumulated depreciation		182
Inventories at 1 October 20-3	2,043	
Trade and other payables		1,309
Purchases	7,854	
Provision for doubtful receivables		72
	21,931	21,931

Further information:

· The inventories at the close of business on 30 September 20-4 cost £2,422,000.

· The corporation tax charge for the year has been calculated as £548,000.

· The land has been revalued by professional valuers at £4,000,000. The revaluation is to be included in the financial statements for the year ended 30 September 20-4.

· All of the operations are continuing operations.

REQUIRED

(a) Draft the statement of comprehensive income for Quine Ltd for the year ended 30 September 20-4.

(b) Draft the statement of financial position for Quine Ltd as at 30 September 20-4.

Note:

Additional notes and disclosures are not required.

3.8 You have been asked to help prepare the financial statements of Nathan Ltd for the year ended 31 March 20X1. The company's trial balance as at 31 March 20X1 is shown below.

Nathan Ltd
Trial balance as at 31 March 20X1

	Debit £000	Credit £000
Share capital		7,000
Trade and other payables		1,010
Plant and equipment – cost	20,500	
accumulated depreciation at 1 April 20X0		4,600
Trade and other receivables	1,546	
Accruals		85
5% bank loan repayable 20X8		3,000
Cash and cash equivalents	185	
Retained earnings		2,537
Interest paid	75	
Sales		21,495
Purchases	9,364	
Returns inwards	186	
Returns outwards		47
Distribution costs	3,852	
Administrative expenses	2,975	
Inventories at 1 April 20X0	641	
Dividends paid	450	
	39,774	39,774

Further information:
- The inventories at the close of business on 31 March 20X1 cost £627,000.
- Depreciation is to be provided on plant and equipment for the year to 31 March 20X1 at 20% per annum using the reducing balance basis. Depreciation is apportioned 60% to distribution costs and 40% to administrative expenses.
- The company hired computers for the period 1 March to 30 June 20X1. The contract price for the four months was £48,000 and this was paid in full on 10 March.
- Interest on the bank loan for the last six months of the year was not paid until 30 April 20X1.
- The corporation tax charge for the year has been calculated as £507,000.
- All of the operations are continuing operations.

(a) **Draft the statement of comprehensive income for Nathan Ltd for the year ended 31 March 20X1.**

(b) **Draft the statement of financial position for Nathan Ltd as at 31 March 20X1.**

Note:
Additional notes and disclosures are not required.

4 Chapter activities
Accounting for assets

4.1   Task 1

What are the two criteria stated by IAS 16, *Property, Plant and Equipment*, for an item of PPE to be recognised as an asset?

Task 2

IAS 16 states that, initially, PPE are measured at cost on the statement of financial position.

(a)   Explain what is meant by 'cost'

(b)   State two attributable costs which *can be included* in the cost of an asset

(c)   State two costs which *cannot be included* in the cost of an asset

(d)   Briefly explain the two models from which an entity must choose as its accounting policy after acquisition of PPE

4.2   With reference to IAS 16, *Property, Plant and Equipment*, you are to:

(a)   Define depreciation.

(b)   Summarise the points a company must consider when accounting for IAS 16.

4.3   According to IAS 38, *Intangible Assets*, which one of the following is not a criteria for capitalising development costs by a business entity?

	✔
the entity intends to complete the intangible asset and to use or sell it	
the entity has no specific aim or application for the intangible asset	
the entity has the resources available to complete the development and to use or sell the intangible asset	
the entity has the ability to measure the development expenditure reliably	

4.4 IAS 38, *Intangible Assets*, gives three key elements of an intangible asset. Which one of the following is not one of the three key elements?

	✔
reliability	
identifiability	
control	
future economic benefits	

4.5 The directors of Tanhosier Ltd are about to undertake the development of a new product. They expect the costs of development to be significant and are concerned at the impact that this might have on their financial statements.

You have been asked to prepare notes to deal with the following queries of the directors:

(a) What is an intangible asset?

(b) What would have to be demonstrated by Tanhosier Ltd before an intangible asset arising from development is recognised as an intangible asset in the financial statements?

4.6 To which of the following assets does IAS 36, *Impairment of Assets*, normally apply?
1   land and buildings
2   inventories
3   goodwill
4   assets held for sale

	✔
all of them	
1 and 2	
1, 2 and 3	
1 and 3	

4.7 **Task 1**

Identify *two* external and *two* internal indicators of impairment.

Task 2

(a)   Explain what is meant by an impairment review.

(b)   How is an impairment review carried out?

4.8   A business has four assets which the directors wish to test for impairment:

asset	carrying amount £	fair value, less costs to sell £	value in use £
1	12,000	11,000	10,000
2	8,000	8,000	9,000
3	15,000	12,000	14,000
4	17,000	19,000	18,000

Which of the above assets is impaired according to IAS 36 *Impairment of Assets*?

	✔
1	
2	
1 and 3	
2 and 4	

4.9   Valdez Limited owns the freehold of a building which it constructed for investment purposes. The building is currently rented to another company on commercial terms. The property is not recorded at its historical cost and has not been depreciated.

Task

Prepare notes for a meeting with the directors of Valdez Limited to explain the accounting treatment of this property.

4.10   With reference to IAS 20, *Accounting for Government Grants and Disclosure of Government Assistance*, you are to:

(a)   Distinguish between

- grants related to assets

- grants related to income

(b)   Explain the general principle of accounting for grants.

(c)   Describe the alternative accounting treatments for grants related to assets.

4.11   (a)   Explain the two inventory valuation methods allowed by IAS 2, *Inventories*.

(b)   Which method of inventory valuation cannot be used under IAS 2?

4.12   Which one of the following statements best describes the valuation of inventories under IAS 2 *Inventories* at the end of the financial year?

✔

at the lower of FIFO and LIFO	
at the lower of cost and net realisable value	
at the higher of FIFO and AVCO	
at the higher of cost and net realisable value	

4.13   You have been asked to assist the directors of Lawnderer Limited, a company that markets and distributes lawnmowers and other garden machinery, in the preparation of the financial statements for the year ended 30 September 20-5.

The directors of the company have had a meeting with you regarding the possible treatment of certain future expenditure in the financial statements of the company. They have told you that the company has been approached by an inventor who has an idea to develop a revolutionary new lawnmower. The project looks technically feasible and preliminary marketing studies suggest a significant market for that product. Cost and revenue projections suggest that future profits should adequately cover the cost of development and have a beneficial effect on the future profitability of the company. The directors are concerned about the effect that the expenditure on developing the new product will have on future profits, given that it will take some time between commencing the project and commercial production.

Task

Explain how the costs of developing the new lawnmower will be reflected in the future financial statements of the company.

Chapter activities

5

Accounting for liabilities and the statement of comprehensive income

5.1 Barrios Limited has a tax expense from its ordinary activities of £25,000 for the year ended 31 March 20X1. Where is this recognised in the year end financial statements?

	✔
in the statement of comprehensive income only	
in the statement of comprehensive income and as a non-current liability in the statement of financial position	
in the statement of comprehensive income and as a current liability in the statement of financial position	
as a current liability in the statement of financial position only	

5.2 Under IAS 17, *Leases*, how should finance leases be recognised as liabilities on a lessee's statement of financial position?

	✔
at the lower of cost and net realisable value of the asset being leased	
at the lower of the fair value of the asset being leased and the present value of the minimum lease payments	
at the higher of the fair value of the asset being leased and its value in use	
at the carrying amount of the asset being leased	

5.3 With reference to IAS 37, *Provisions, Contingent Liabilities and Contingent Assets*, you are to:

    (a)   Define

- provisions
- contingent liabilities
- contingent assets

    (b)   Explain for each the accounting treatment, if any, in the year end financial statements.

5.4 A business prepares its financial statements to 31 December each year. The following events took place after 31 December but before the date on which the financial statements were authorised for issue:

1. a significant part of the business is to be discontinued

2. the net realisable value of inventories is found to be materially below the cost price used in the financial statements

Which of the above is likely to be classified as an adjusting event under IAS 10, *Events after the Reporting Period*?

	✔
1 only	
2 only	
1 and 2	
neither 1 nor 2	

5.5 A major customer who owes money to a company at the end of the financial year is declared bankrupt before the date of authorising the financial statements for issue. Under IAS 10, *Events after the Reporting Period*, this should be classified as an adjusting event.

	✔
True	
False	

5.6 Prepare notes for a meeting with the directors of Cortez Limited to explain the accounting treatment of the following issues:

(a) A note to the accounts states that there was a fire in the warehouse of the company that occurred after the year end and resulted in considerable losses of non-current assets and inventories. No adjustment for these losses appears to have been made in the year end financial statements.

(b) There is a non-current liability for something called "deferred tax" in the statement of financial position of the company.

Note: You should make reference, where appropriate, to relevant international accounting standards.

5.7 With reference to IAS 18, *Revenue*, you are to:

(a) Explain what is meant by revenue. Give two examples of revenue, other than the sale of goods.

(b) State how revenue is to be measured.

(c) Explain when revenue from the sale of goods should be recognised.

5.8 For the earnings per share calculation required by IAS 33, *Earnings per Share*, the amount of the total comprehensive income for the year is calculated after allowing for which of the following?

1 finance costs

2 tax

3 non-controlling interests

4 dividends on preference shares

	✔
all of them	
1 and 2	
2 and 3	
2, 3 and 4	

5.9 The statement of comprehensive income (extract) of Kingston plc for the year to 31 December 20-8 is as follows:

	£000
Continuing operations	
Profit before tax	960
Tax	(210)
Profit for the year from continuing operations	750
Discontinued operations	
Profit for the year from discontinued operations	60
Total comprehensive income for the year	810

The company's share capital at 31 December 20-8 is £40m ordinary shares of £1 each. No new shares were issued during the year.

Task 1

You are asked to calculate the basic earnings per share of Kingston plc for 20-8.

Task 2

The company did consider making a new issue of £10m ordinary shares of £1 each at full market value on 1 October 20-8. Although the issue did not go ahead, the finance director asks you to calculate what the EPS figure would have been for the year.

Note: calculate EPS in pence per share, to two decimal places.

5.10 Which of the following types of segments are identified in IFRS 8, *Operating Segments*?

1 political segment
2 operating segment
3 reportable segment
4 customer segment

	✔
all of them	
1 and 2	
2 and 3	
3 and 4	

6

Chapter activities

Statement of cash flows

A layout for a statement of cash flows and a statement of changes in equity is included in the Appendix of *Limited company accounts tutorial*, and is also available in the Resources section of www.osbornebooks.co.uk.

6.1   Rowan Ltd has a profit from operations of £30,000 for the year and the statement of comprehensive income and statement of financial position show the following:

	£
depreciation charge	10,000
increase in inventories	5,000
decrease in trade and other receivables	4,000
increase in trade and other payables	6,000

What is the cash from operations for the year?

	✔
£45,000 inflow	
£15,000 inflow	
£55,000 inflow	
£25,000 inflow	

6.2 Meadow Ltd has a loss from operations of £10,000 for the year and the statement of comprehensive income and statement of financial position show the following:

	£
depreciation charge	8,000 +
decrease in inventories	4,000 +
increase in trade and other receivables	5,000 −
decrease in trade and other payables	3,000 −

What is the cash from operations for the year?

	✔
£14,000 inflow	
£30,000 inflow	
£14,000 outflow	
£6,000 outflow	

6.3 Boughton Ltd has the following receipts and payments for the year:

	£
cash receipts from customers	600,000
cash payments to suppliers and employees	320,000
interest paid	15,000
tax paid	55,000

What is the cash from operating activities for the year using the direct method?

	✔
£240,000 inflow	
£210,000 inflow	
£320,000 inflow	
£390,000 outflow	

6.4 You have been asked to help prepare the statement of cash flows and statement of changes in equity for Carmen Ltd for the year ended 31 March 20X1.

The most recent statement of comprehensive income and statement of financial position (with comparatives for the previous year) of Carmen Ltd are set out below.

Carmen Ltd – Statement of comprehensive income for the year ended 31 March 20X1

	£000
Continuing operations	
Revenue	33,040
Cost of sales	(14,270)
Gross profit	18,770
Dividends received	30
Loss on disposal of property, plant and equipment	(50)
Distribution costs	(10,210)
Administrative expenses	(6,340)
Profit from operations	2,200
Finance costs	(190)
Profit before tax	2,010
Tax	(350)
Profit for the period from continuing operations	1,660

	20X1 £000	20X0 £000
Assets		
Non-current assets		
Property, plant and equipment	15,350	13,750
Current assets		
Inventories	8,234	7,146
Trade and other receivables	6,827	6,954
Cash and cash equivalents	0	135
	15,061	14,235
Total assets	30,411	27,985
EQUITY AND LIABILITIES		
Equity		
Share capital	10,500	10,000
Share premium	1,200	1,000
Retained earnings	8,973	8,363
Total equity	20,673	19,363
Non-current liabilities		
Bank loans	1,800	2,000
	1,800	2,000
Current liabilities		
Trade and other payables	7,102	6,047
Tax liability	350	575
Bank overdraft	486	0
	7,938	6,622
Total liabilities	9,738	8,622
Total equity and liabilities	30,411	27,985

Further information:

- The total depreciation charge for the year was £2,340,000.
- Property, plant and equipment costing £520,000 with accumulated depreciation of £380,000 was sold in the year.
- All sales and purchases were on credit. Other expenses were paid for in cash.
- A dividend of £1,050,000 was paid during the year.

(a) **Prepare a reconciliation of profit from operations to net cash from operating activities for Carmen Ltd for the year ended 31 March 20X1.**

(b) **Prepare the statement of cash flows for Carmen Ltd for the year ended 31 March 20X1.**

(c) **Draft the statement of changes in equity for Carmen Ltd for the year ended 31 March 20X1.**

6.5 Set out below are financial statements for Underdesk Limited for the year ending 20-7 and also for the previous year.

Underdesk Limited: Statement of comprehensive income for the year ended 31 December

Continuing operations	20-7 £000	20-6 £000
Revenue	5,490	4,573
Cost of sales	(3,861)	(3,201)
Gross profit	1,629	1,372
Depreciation	(672)	(445)
Other expenses	(313)	(297)
Gain on disposal of non-current assets	29	13
Profit from operations	673	643
Finance costs	(156)	(47)
Profit before tax	517	596
Tax	(129)	(124)
Profit for the period from continuing operations	388	472

Underdesk Limited: Statement of financial position as at 31 December

	20-7 £000	20-6 £000
ASSETS		
Non-current assets	5,461	2,979
Current assets		
Inventories	607	543
Trade and other receivables	481	426
Cash and cash equivalents	–	104
	1,088	1,073
Total assets	6,549	4,052
EQUITY AND LIABILITIES		
Equity		
Share capital	1,400	800
Share premium	400	100
Retained earnings	2,460	2,168
Total equity	4,260	3,068
Non-current liabilities		
Long-term loan	1,700	520
	1,700	520
Current liabilities		
Trade and other payables	371	340
Tax liability	129	124
Bank overdraft	89	–
	589	464
Total liabilities	2,289	984
Total equity and liabilities	6,549	4,052

Further information

- A dividend of £96,000 was paid during the year.

- Non-current assets costing £187,000 with accumulated depreciation of £102,000 were disposed in 20-7 for £114,000. There were no other disposals in the year.

- All revenue sales and purchases were on credit. Other expenses were paid for in cash.

REQUIRED

Task 1

Provide a reconciliation of profit from operations to net cash from operating activities for the year ended 31 December 20-7.

Task 2

Prepare the statement of cash flows for Underdesk Limited for the year ended 31 December 20-7 in accordance with the requirements of IAS 7.

7 Chapter activities
Interpretation of financial statements

7.1 A limited company has the following statement of comprehensive income:

	£000
Continuing operations	
Revenue	225
Cost of sales	(140)
Gross profit	85
Distribution costs	(20)
Administrative expenses	(25)
Profit from operations	40
Finance costs	(10)
Profit before tax	30
Tax	(8)
Profit for the period from continuing operations	22

(a) State the formula that is used to calculate each of the following ratios:

    (i) Gross profit percentage

    (ii) Distribution costs/revenue percentage

    (iii) Operating profit percentage

    (iv) Interest cover

(b) Calculate the above ratios (to one decimal place)

7.2 The following information is taken from the statement of financial position of a limited company.

	£000
Inventories	380
Trade receivables	450
Cash and cash equivalents	40
Trade payables	410
Non-current liabilities	320
Share capital	450
Retained earnings	140
Further information:	
Revenue for year	4,390
Cost of sales for year	3,360

(a) **State the formula that is used to calculate each of the following ratios:**

(i) **Current ratio**

(ii) **Acid test (quick) ratio**

(iii) **Inventory turnover**

(iv) **Inventory holding period**

(v) **Trade receivables collection period**

(vi) **Trade payables payment period**

(vii) **Gearing**

(b) **Calculate the above ratios (to one decimal place)**

7.3   The following information is taken from the financial statements of a limited company.

	£000
Revenue	1,450
Profit from operations	120
Profit after tax	90
Total assets	870
Share capital (£1 ordinary shares)	500
Retained earnings	220
Non-current liabilities	100
Current liabilities	50

(a)   **State the formula that is used to calculate each of the following ratios:**

(i)   **Return on capital employed**

(ii)   **Return on total assets**

(iii) **Return on equity**

(iv)   **Earnings per share**

(v)   **Asset turnover (total assets)**

(b)   **Calculate the above ratios (to one decimal place)**

7.4 Bragg plc wants to acquire a majority holding in a private limited company. The Managing Director of Bragg plc has asked you to analyse the financial statements of two possible companies and to deal with some queries he has about financial statements. He has asked you to consider the profitability of the companies and their financial position. The financial statements of the two companies are set out below and on the next page.

**Summary statements of comprehensive income
for the year ended 31 March 20-4**

	Roy Limited	Ishiguro Limited
	£000	£000
Continuing operations		
Revenue	8,483	10,471
Cost of sales	(3,732)	(5,026)
Gross profit	4,751	5,445
Distribution costs	(1,218)	(1,483)
Administrative expenses	(903)	(1,658)
Profit from operations	2,630	2,304
Finance costs	(160)	(520)
Profit before tax	2,470	1,784
Tax	(593)	(428)
Profit for the period from continuing operations	1,877	1,356
Dividends paid in year	400	800

Statements of financial position as at 31 March 20-4

	Roy Limited	Ishiguro Limited
	£000	£000
ASSETS		
Non-current assets	6,806	12,579
Current assets		
Inventories	2,531	2,181
Trade receivables	1,054	2,309
Cash and cash equivalents	828	5
	4,413	4,495
Total assets	11,219	17,074
EQUITY AND LIABILITIES		
Equity		
Share capital	2,000	2,000
Share premium	1,000	500
Retained earnings	4,367	4,997
Total equity	7,367	7,497
Non-current liabilities		
Long-term loan	2,000	6,500
	2,000	6,500
Current liabilities		
Trade payables	1,259	2,166
Bank overdraft	–	483
Tax liability	593	428
	1,852	3,077
Total liabilities	3,852	9,577
Total equity and liabilities	11,219	17,074

REQUIRED

Prepare a report for Bragg plc that includes the following:

(a)   a calculation of the following four ratios of Roy Limited and Ishiguro Limited:

return on equity, gross profit percentage, gearing ratio, interest cover

(b)   an explanation of the meaning of each ratio and a comment on the relative profitability and financial position of the two companies based on the ratios calculated

(c)   a conclusion as to which company to invest in, based only on these ratios and your analysis

7.5 The directors of Mercia Printers Ltd, a medium-sized printing firm, have recently read the industry's trade magazine and seen an article quoting the following average ratios for the printing sector:

Return on capital employed	16%
Gearing ratio	21%
Current ratio	1.8:1
Operating profit percentage	8%
Trade payables payment period	62 days

The magazine article discusses the benefits of printing companies benchmarking their own performance against the sector's industrial average in order to assess overall performance and efficiency.

Mercia Printers Limited's statement of comprehensive income and statement of financial position are set out below and on the next page.

Mercia Printers Limited

Statement of comprehensive income for the year ended 31 August 20-4

	£000
Continuing operations	
Revenue	2,750
Cost of sales	(2,200)
Gross profit	550
Distribution costs	(140)
Administrative expenses	(210)
Profit from operations	200
Finance costs	(63)
Profit before tax	137
Tax	(41)
Profit for the period from continuing operations	96

Mercia Printers Limited

Statement of financial position as at 31 August 20-4

ASSETS	£000
Non-current assets	450
Current assets	
Inventories	215
Trade receivables	352
Cash and cash equivalents	13
	580
Total assets	1,030
EQUITY AND LIABILITIES	
Equity	
Share capital	240
Retained earnings	366
Total equity	606
Non-current liabilities	250
	250
Current liabilities	
Trade payables	133
Tax liability	41
	174
Total liabilities	424
Total equity and liabilities	1,030

REQUIRED

Write a report for the directors of Mercia Printers Limited, assessing the performance of the company.

The draft report should include:

(a)   A calculation from the financial statements of Mercia Printers Limited of the appropriate ratios listed in the magazine article (see above). You should quote the formulas used and show detailed workings for each ratio.

(b)   An assessment of the company's overall performance, comparing its ratios with the sector average.

8   Chapter activities
Consolidated financial statements

A layout for a consolidated statement of comprehensive income and a consolidated statement of financial position is included in the Appendix of *Limited company accounts tutorial*, and is also available in the Resources section of www.osbornebooks.co.uk.

8.1   Wyvern plc invested £260,000 in 150,000 ordinary shares of £1 each in Sidbury Limited. At the date of acquisition the equity of Sidbury Limited comprised £200,000 in share capital and £120,000 in retained earnings.

What is the value of goodwill at the date of acquisition?

	✔
£240,000	
£20,000	
£60,000	
£50,000	

8.2   At 31 March 20X1 the equity of Teme Limited comprises £100,000 in share capital and £80,000 in retained earnings. The parent company, Severn plc, currently owns 60,000 of £1 ordinary shares in Teme Limited.

What is the value of the non-controlling interest at 31 March 20X1?

	✔
£180,000	
£108,000	
£80,000	
£72,000	

8.3 Star plc owns 70% of the ordinary shares in Buck Limited. Revenue for the year ended 31 March 20X1 is: Star £500,000, Buck £140,000. The revenue of Star plc includes goods sold to Buck Limited for £20,000. All of these goods still remain in the inventory of Buck Limited at the end of the year.

What is the value for revenue that will be shown in the consolidated statement of comprehensive income for Star plc and its subsidiary undertaking for the year ended 31 March 20X1?

	✔
£640,000	
£661,000	
£620,000	
£626,000	

8.4 IFRS 3, *Business Combinations*, identifies a number of features in the preparation of consolidated financial statements. Explain the following:

·   method of accounting to be used in acquisitions

·   assets and liabilities acquired

·   goodwill

8.5 (a)   In business combinations, how are fair values to be treated on acquisition?

(b)   What effect do fair values have on the calculations for:

·   goodwill

·   non-controlling interest

·   post-acquisition profits

8.6 You have been asked to assist in the preparation of the consolidated financial statements of the Shopan Group. Set out below are the statements of financial position of Shopan Limited and its subsidiary undertaking Hower Limited, as at 30 September 20-9:

Statements of financial position as at 30 September 20-9

	Shopan Limited	Hower Limited
ASSETS	£000	£000
Non-current assets	6,273	1,633
Investment in Hower Limited	2,100	
Current assets		
Inventories	1,901	865
Trade receivables	1,555	547
Cash and cash equivalents	184	104
	3,640	1,516
Total assets	12,013	3,149
EQUITY AND LIABILITIES		
Equity		
Share capital	2,000	500
Share premium	950	120
Retained earnings	4,246	1,484
Total equity	7,196	2,104
Non-current liabilities		
Loan	2,870	400
Current liabilities		
Trade payables	1,516	457
Tax liability	431	188
	1,947	645
Total liabilities	4,817	1,045
Total equity and liabilities	12,013	3,149

Further information

- The share capital of both Shopan Limited and Hower Limited consists of ordinary shares of £1 each.
- Shopan Limited acquired 375,000 shares in Hower Limited on 30 September 20-9.
- The fair value of the non-current assets of Hower Limited at 30 September 20-9 was £2,033,000.   400 + air value.
- Shopan Limited has decided non-controlling interest will be valued at their proportionate share of net assets.

REQUIRED

Task 1
Prepare the consolidated statement of financial position for Shopan Limited and its subsidiary undertaking as at 30 September 20-9.

Task 2
IFRS 3, *Business Combinations*, defines control over another business as 'the power to govern the financial and operating policies of an entity or business so as to obtain benefits from its activities'. Give two of the criteria that, according to IFRS 3, give control of an entity.

8.7 The Finance Director of Fairway plc has asked you to prepare the draft consolidated statement of comprehensive income for the group. The company has one subsidiary, Green Limited. The statements of comprehensive income of the two companies, prepared for internal purposes, for the year ended 30 June 20-2 are set out below:

Statements of comprehensive income for the year ended 30 June 20-2

	Fairway plc	Green Limited
Continuing operations	£000	£000
Revenue	12,200	4,400
Cost of sales	(8,500)	(3,100)
Gross profit	3,700	1,300
Distribution costs	(1,600)	(500)
Administrative expenses	(400)	(200)
Dividends received from Green Limited	80	–
Profit from operations	1,780	600
Finance costs	(300)	(200)
Profit before tax	1,480	400
Tax	(400)	(100)
Profit for the period from continuing operations	1,080	300

Further information

- Fairway plc acquired 80% of the ordinary share capital of Green Limited on 1 July 20-1.

- During the year Green Limited sold goods which had cost £750,000 to Fairway plc for £1,000,000. All the goods had been sold by Fairway plc by the end of the year.

- Dividends paid during the year were:
  Fairway plc, £700,000
  Green Limited, £100,000

- There were no impairment losses on goodwill during the year.

REQUIRED

Draft a consolidated statement of comprehensive income for Fairway plc and its subsidiary undertaking for the year ended 30 June 20-2.

8.8 Perran Plc acquired 80% of the issued share capital of Porth Ltd on 1 April 20X0 for £750,000. At that date Porth Ltd had issued share capital of £600,000 and retained earnings of £240,000.

Extracts from the statements of financial position for the two companies one year later at 31 March 20X1 are as follows:

	Perran Plc £000	Porth Ltd £000
Assets		
Investment in Porth Ltd	750	
Non-current assets	770	800
Current assets	450	350
Total assets	1,970	1,150
Equity and liabilities		
Equity		
Share capital	1,000	600
Retained earnings	450	300
Total equity	1,450	900
Non-current liabilities	120	50
Current liabilities	400	200
Total liabilities	520	250
Total equity and liabilities	1,970	1,150

Additional data

• Included within the current assets of Perran Plc and in the current liabilities of Porth Ltd is an inter-company transaction for £70,000 that took place in early March 20X1.

• Perran Plc has decided non-controlling interest will be valued at their proportionate share of net assets.

(a)   **Draft the consolidated statement of financial position for Perran Plc and its subsidiary undertaking as at 31 March 20X1.**

Fistral Plc acquired 75% of the issued share capital of Beach Ltd on 1 April 20X0.

Extracts from their statements of comprehensive income for the year ended 31 March 20X1 are shown below:

	Fistral Plc £000	Beach Ltd £000
Continuing operations		
Revenue	18,250	6,450
Cost of sales	(11,800)	(3,100)
Gross profit	6,450	3,350
Other income – dividend from Beach Ltd	400	–
Distribution costs and administrative expenses	(3,750)	(1,650)
Profit before tax	3,100	1,700

Additional data

During the year Beach Ltd sold goods which had cost £50,000 to Fistral Plc for £90,000. Half of these goods still remain in inventory at the end of the year.

(b)   **Draft the consolidated statement of comprehensive income for Fistral Plc and its subsidiary undertaking up to and including the profit before tax line for the year ended 31 March 20X1.**

Answers to
chapter activities

Chapter activities – answers
Purpose of financial statements

1 (left margin block number)

1.1 **(a)** According to the *Framework for the Preparation and Presentation of Financial Statements* the objective of financial statements is:

- 'to provide information

- about the financial position, performance and changes in financial position of an entity

- that is useful to a wide range of users

- in making economic decisions'

(b) Two examples of external users of financial statements and their purposes in using financial statement information include:

User	Purpose
Present and potential investors	To enable them to assess how effectively management has fulfilled its stewardship role and to consider information that is useful in taking decisions about their investment or potential investment in the entity
Lenders, such as banks	To assess whether loans will be repaid and related interest will be repaid when due/to help potential investors decide whether to lend and on what terms
Suppliers	To decide whether to sell to the entity and to assess the likelihood that amounts owing will be paid when due
Employees	To enable them to assess their employer's ability to provide remuneration, employment opportunities and retirement and other benefits
Customers	To find out about the continued existence of the entity where they may have long-term involvement or are dependent on the entity
Governments and their agencies	To assist them in regulating the activities of the entity, assessing taxation and providing a basis for national statistics
The public	To assess trends and recent developments in the entity's prosperity and range of activities

1.2 income – expenses = profits or losses

1.3 £35,250 – £14,600 = £20,650

1.4

Statement	Characteristic
Financial information that is useful to users of the financial statements	Relevance
Financial information that can be depended upon by users	Reliability
Financial statements that can be compared with those from previous years	Comparability
Users of financial statements can understand the information given	Understandability

1.5   (a)   The accounting equation is:

Assets – Liabilities = Equity

The elements are defined as follows:

- assets – resources controlled by the entity as a result of past events and from which future economic benefits are expected to flow to the entity

- liabilities – present obligations of the entity arising from past events, the settlement of which is expected to result in an outflow from the entity of resources embodying economic benefits

- equity – the residual interest in the assets of the entity after deducting all its liabilities

(b)
- profit for the year increases the equity in the accounting equation

- this is matched by an increase in the assets of the business that amount to the difference between assets minus liabilities

1.6   (a)   The elements that appear in financial statements according to the *Framework for the Preparation and Presentation of Financial Statements* are:

- assets
- liabilities
- equity
- income
- expenses

(b)   The elements that appear in the statement of comprehensive income are:

- income
- expenses

Income is increases in economic benefits during the accounting period in the form of inflows or enhancements of assets, or decreases of liabilities that result in increases in equity, other than those relating to contributions from equity participants.

Expenses are decreases in economic benefits during the accounting period in the form of outflows or depletions of assets or incurring of liabilities that result in decreases in equity, other than those relating to distributions to equity participants.

2 Chapter activities – answers
Introduction to limited company financial statements

2.1   (a)   *Public limited company (plc)*

A company may become a public limited company if it has:

- issued share capital of over £50,000

- at least two members (shareholders) and at least two directors

A public limited company may raise capital from the public on the Stock Exchange or similar markets, but not all do so.

  (b)   *Private limited company (ltd)*

A private limited company is defined by the Companies Act 2006 as 'any company that is not a public company'.

A private limited company has:

- no minimum requirement for issued share capital

- at least one member (shareholder) and at least one director who may be the sole shareholder

The shares of a private limited company are not traded publicly on the Stock Exchange or similar markets, but are transferable between individuals.

2.2   anyone taking legal action proceeds against the company and not the individual shareholders

2.3   ordinary shares

2.4   £55,000

2.5   Crantock plc – Statement of comprehensive income for the year ending 31 March 20-2

Continuing operations	£000	£000
Revenue		2,295
Opening inventories	160	
Purchases	1,200	
Less Closing inventories	180	
Cost of sales		(1,180)
Gross profit		1,115
Overheads:		
Administrative expenses	(240)	
Distribution costs	(500)	
		(740)
Profit before tax		375
Tax		(65)
Profit for the year from continuing operations		310

Crantock plc – Statement of financial position as at 31 March 20-2

	Cost	Dep'n	Net
ASSETS	£000	£000	£000
Non-current assets			
Plant and equipment	1,600	500	1,100
Current assets			
Inventories			180
Trade receivables			525
Cash and cash equivalents			75
			780
Total assets			1,880
EQUITY AND LIABILITIES			
Equity			
Share capital			700
Share premium			200
Retained earnings			520
Total equity			1,420
Current liabilities			
Trade payables			395
Tax liability			65
Total liabilities			460
Total equity and liabilities			1,880

Tutorial note (£000):

Retained earnings

Trial balance	350
+ Profit for the year	310
– Dividends paid	140
	520

2.6   Playfair Ltd – Statement of comprehensive income for the year ending 31 December 20-3

Continuing operations	£000	£000
Revenue		2,340
Opening inventories	250	
Purchases	1,650	
Less Closing inventories	280	
Cost of sales		(1,620)
Gross profit		720
Overheads:		
Administrative expenses	(210)	
Distribution costs	(320)	
		(530)
Profit from operations		190
Finance costs		(40)
Profit before tax		150
Tax		(30)
Profit for the year from continuing operations		120

Playfair Ltd – Statement of financial position as at 31 December 20-3

	Cost	Dep'n	Net
ASSETS	£000	£000	£000
Non-current assets			
Land	500	–	500
Plant and equipment	800	390	410
	1,300	390	910
Current assets			
Inventories			280
Trade and other receivables			350
Cash and cash equivalents			140
			770
Total assets			1,680
EQUITY AND LIABILITIES			
Equity			
Share capital			580
Share premium			50
Retained earnings			610
Total equity			1,240
Non-current liabilities			
Long-term loan			200
			200
Current liabilities			
Trade and other payables			210
Tax liability			30
			240
Total liabilities			440
Total equity and liabilities			1,680

Tutorial note (£000):

Depreciation of plant and equipment

Plant and equipment at cost	800
20% depreciation	160
Allocated to	
Distribution costs	80
Administrative expenses	80
	160

Accumulated depreciation

230 + 160	=	390

Administrative expenses

Trial balance	110
+ Depreciation of plant and equipment	80
+ Increase in provision for doubtful receivables	20
	210

Distribution costs

Trial balance	240
+ Depreciation of plant and equipment	80
	320

Finance costs

Trial balance	20
+ Interest accrued	20
	40

Trade and other receivables

Trial balance	350
+ Prepayments	40
– Provision for doubtful receivables	40
	350

Retained earnings

Trial balance	540
+ Profit for the year	120
– Dividends paid	50
	610

Trade and other payables

Trial balance	160
+ Accruals	30
+ Interest accrued	20
	210

3   Chapter activities – answers
Pubished financial statements of limited companies

3.1   'The objective of financial statements is to provide *information* about the *financial* position, financial *performance* and *cash* flows of an entity that is *useful* to a wide range of *users* in making *economic* decisions.'

3.2   1. statement of comprehensive income; 2. statement of cash flows; 4. statement of changes in equity

3.3   (i) nine months   (ii) six months

3.4   1. revaluation reserve;   3. share premium

3.5   1. a rights issue of shares

3.6   *Accounting policies* are the specific accounting bases selected by the directors of a company and followed by a company.

Examples include the method of depreciation, inventory valuation, valuation of non-current assets.

3.7 (a)

Quine Ltd – Statement of comprehensive income for the year ended 30 September 20-4	
	£000
Continuing operations	
Revenue	10,884
Cost of sales	(7,475)
Gross profit	3,409
Distribution costs	(980)
Administrative expenses	(461)
Profit from operations	1,968
Finance costs	(200)
Profit before tax	1,768
Tax	(548)
Profit for the period from continuing operations	1,220
Other comprehensive income for the year	
Gain on revaluation of the land (4,000 – 3,600)	400
Total comprehensive income for the year	1,620

(b)

Quine Ltd – Statement of financial position as at 30 September 20-4	
	£000
ASSETS	
Non-current assets	
Property, plant and equipment	6,100
Current assets	
Inventories	2,422
Trade and other receivables	1,814
Cash and cash equivalents	103
	4,339
Total assets	10,439
EQUITY AND LIABILITIES	
Equity	
Share capital	3,000
Share premium	500
Revaluation reserve	400
Retained earnings	2,077
Total equity	5,977
Non-current liabilities	
Bank loan	2,500
	2,500
Current liabilities	
Trade and other payables	1,414
Tax liability	548
	1,962
Total liabilities	4,462
Total equity and liabilities	10,439

Tutorial notes (£000):

Cost of sales

Opening inventories	2,043
+ Purchases	7,854
− Closing inventories	2,422
	7,475

Non-current assets

Property, plant and equipment	Cost/ Revaluation	Accumulated depreciation	Carrying amount
Land	4,000	–	4,000
Buildings	1,480	702	778
Fixtures and fittings	645	317	328
Vehicles	1,632	903	729
Office equipment	447	182	265
	8,204	2,104	6,100

Trade and other receivables

Trade receivables	1,802
− Provision for doubtful trade receivables	72
+ Prepayments	84
	1,814

Revaluation reserve: £4,000 (revaluation) − £3,600 (cost) = £400

Retained earnings

Trial balance	1,457
+ Profit for period	1,220
− Dividends paid	600
	2,077

Trade and other payables

Trade payables	1,309
+ Accruals	105
	1,414

3.8 (a)

Nathan Ltd – Statement of comprehensive income for the year ended 31 March 20X1.	
	£000
Continuing operations	
Revenue	21,309
Cost of sales	(9,331)
Gross profit	11,978
Distribution costs	(5,760)
Administrative expenses	(4,211)
Profit from operations	2,007
Finance costs	(150)
Profit before tax	1,857
Tax	(507)
Profit for the period from continuing operations	1,350

(b)

Nathan Ltd – Statement of financial position as at 31 March 20X1.	£000
ASSETS	
Non-current assets	
Plant and equipment	12,720
Current assets	
Inventories	627
Trade and other receivables	1,582
Cash and cash equivalents	185
	2,394
Total assets	15,114
EQUITY AND LIABILITIES	
Equity	
Share capital	7,000
Retained earnings	3,437
Total equity	10,437
Non-current liabilities	
Bank loan	3,000
	3,000
Current liabilities	
Trade and other payables	1,170
Tax liability	507
	1,677
Total liabilities	4,677
Total equity and liabilities	15,114

Tutorial notes:

		£000
Revenue		
Sales		21,495
– Returns in		186
		21,309
Cost of sales		
Opening inventories		641
+ Purchases	9,364	
– Returns out	47	9,317
– Closing inventories		627
		9,331

Distribution costs	*£000*
Trial balance	3,852
+ Depreciation 20% x (£20,500 – £4,600) x 60%	1,908
	5,760

Administrative expenses	
Trial balance	2,975
– Prepayment	36
+ Depreciation 20% x (£20,500 – £4,600) x 40%	1,272
	4,211

Finance costs	
Trial balance	75
+ Accrual	75
	150

Non-current assets	
Plant and equipment per trial balance	20,500
– Accumulated depreciation to 1 April 20X0	4,600
	15,900
– Depreciation for year 20% x £15,900	3,180
	12,720

Trade and other receivables	
Trial balance	1,546
+ Prepayment for hire of computers	36
	1,582

Retained earnings	
Trial balance	2,537
+ Profit for period	1,350
– Dividends paid	450
	3,437

Trade and other payables	
Trial balance	1,010
+ Trial balance accruals	85
+ Interest accrued	75
	1,170

4

Chapter activities – answers
Accounting for assets

4.1 Task 1

Two criteria for recognition of an item of PPE:

- it is probable that *future economic benefits* will flow to the entity
- the cost of the asset can be *measured reliably*

Task 2

(a) Cost is the purchase price of the asset, including any import duties, plus any costs directly attributable to bring the asset to the location and condition for its intended use, plus the estimated costs of dismantling and removing the asset at the end of its useful life.

(b) *Attributable costs which can be included in the cost of an asset*

Two from:

- costs of site preparation
- initial delivery and handling costs
- installation and assembly costs
- costs of testing the asset
- professional fees, eg engineers, architects

(c) *Costs which cannot be included in the cost of an asset*

Two from:

- administration and other general overhead costs
- start-up costs of a new business or section of the business
- start-up costs for introducing a new product or service – such as advertising and promotional costs

(d) Two models to choose from:

- *Cost model* – the asset is carried at cost less accumulated depreciation and impairment losses
- *Revaluation model* – the asset is carried at a revalued amount, being its fair value less any subsequent depreciation and impairment losses; revaluations are to be made regularly to ensure that the carrying amount does not differ materially from its fair value at the date of the statement of financial position.

4.2 (a)   IAS 16, *Property, Plant and Equipment*, defines depreciation as the systematic allocation of the depreciable amount of an asset over its useful life. (Depreciable amount is the cost or valuation of the asset, less any residual value.)

(b) •   IAS 16 states that, initially, PPE are to be measured at cost in the statement of financial position.

•   After acquisition of PPE an entity must choose either the cost model or the revaluation model as its accounting policy – which is then applied to an entire class of PPE.

•   Using the cost model, assets are carried in the statement of financial position at cost less accumulated depreciation and impairment losses.

•   Using the revaluation model, assets are carried at a revalued amount, being fair value less any subsequent depreciation and impairment losses; revaluations are to be made regularly to ensure that the carrying amounts do not differ materially from fair values at the date of the statement of financial position.

•   The residual value and the useful life of an asset are to be reviewed at least annually.

•   Depreciation continues to be recognised even if the fair value of an asset exceeds its carrying amount (but there is no need for depreciation when the residual value is greater than the carrying amount).

•   Spending money on repair and maintenance of an asset does not remove the need for depreciation.

•   When calculating depreciable amount, the residual values of assets are often low or immaterial – for example, the scrap value of a machine is often negligible.

•   Depreciation can be applied to separate parts of an asset where each part is a significant cost – for example, the engines of an aircraft are often depreciated separately from the body of the aircraft.

•   Depreciation for the period is recognised in the statement of comprehensive income (unless it is included in the carrying amount of another asset).

•   When determining the useful life of an asset, the following factors need to be considered (even if the asset is not being used):

–   expected usage of the asset, ie the expected capacity or output

–   expected physical wear and tear, which depends on operational factors and the repair and maintenance programme

–   technical or commercial obsolescence, eg the introduction of new technology, changes in demand for the product or service

–   legal or similar limits on the use of the asset, eg the period for which an asset is leased

4.3   the entity has no specific aim or application for the intangible asset

4.4   reliability

4.5   (a)   IAS 38, *Intangible Assets*, defines an intangible asset as

· an identifiable non-monetary asset

· without physical substance

(b)   Before an intangible asset arising from development is recognised as an intangible asset in the financial statements of Tanhosier Ltd they would have to demonstrate:

· the technical feasibility of completing the intangible asset so that it will be available for use or sale

· the intention to complete the intangible asset and to use or sell it

· its ability to use or sell the intangible asset

· the way in which the intangible asset will generate probable future economic benefits

· the availability of resources to complete the development and to use or sell the intangible asset

· its ability to measure reliably the expenditure attributable to the intangible asset

4.6   1. land and buildings; 3. goodwill

4.7   **Task 1**

External indicators

Two from:

- a significant fall in the asset's market value

- adverse effects on the entity caused by technology, markets, the economy, laws

- increases in interest rates

- the stock market value of the entity is less than the carrying amount of net assets

Internal indicators

Two from:

- obsolescence or physical damage to the asset

- adverse effects on the asset of a significant reorganisation within the entity

- the economic performance of the asset is worse than expected

Note: Other indicators – such as evidence from internal financial statements – can indicate that an asset may be impaired.

Examples include:

- a fall in the profit (or an increase in the loss) from operations

- a fall in the cash flows from operations, or a negative cash flow

- a fall in budgeted cash flows, or budgeted profit from operations

Task 2

(a)   An impairment review involves comparing the asset's carrying amount with the recoverable amount.

(b)   An impairment review is carried out in three steps:

Step 1   Identify the asset's carrying amount (net book value, ie cost/revaluation less depreciation/amortisation to date)

Step 2   Identify the asset's recoverable amount, ie the higher of fair value less costs to sell (the net realisable value of the asset) and value is use (the present value of the future cash flows from an asset's continued use, including cash from disposal).

Step 3   If carrying amount is greater than recoverable amount, then the asset is impaired and should be written down to its recoverable amount in the statement of financial position. The amount of the impairment loss is recognised as an expense in the statement of comprehensive income unless it relates to a previously revalued asset, when it is debited to the revaluation surplus within equity (to the extent of the revaluation surplus for that particular asset).

4.8   1 and 3

4.9   **Notes for the directors of Valdez Limited**

The freehold building meets the definition of an investment property given in IAS 40, *Investment Property*, ie property held to earn rent or for capital appreciation, but not being used in the ordinary course of business.

IAS 40 requires that, initially, investment property is to be measured at cost. After acquisition an entity must choose either the fair value model or the cost model. Under the fair value model, the investment property is measured at fair value, with any gain or loss arising from a change in fair value being recognised in the statement of comprehensive income for the period to which it relates. Under the cost model, the investment property is measured at cost less accumulated depreciation and impairment losses.

It would seem that, here, the company has adopted the fair value model as its accounting policy – this explains why the property is not recorded at its historical cost and has not been depreciated.

4.10   (a)   •   *grants related to assets* are government grants whose primary condition is that an entity qualifying for them should purchase, construct or otherwise acquire long-term assets

           •   *grants related to income* are government grants other than those related to assets

        (b)   The general principles of accounting for grants are:

           •   government grants are not to be recognised in the financial statements until it is reasonably certain that:

                –   the business receiving the grant will comply with the conditions of the grants, and

                –   the grant will be received

           •   for grants related to assets, the grant is to be recognised as income over the expected useful life of the asset

        (c)   The alternative accounting treatments for grants related to assets are:

           •   either to treat the amount of the grant as a deferred credit, a portion of which is credited to each year's statement of comprehensive income (with the remaining amount of the deferred credit shown as a liability in the statement of financial position)

           •   or to reduce the carrying amount of the non-current asset acquired by the amount of the grant (this means that the annual depreciation of the non-current asset will be reduced and, in this way, the grant will be recognised as income)

        These alternative treatments are often referred to as the 'gross method' and 'net method' respectively. They both achieve the same financial result in that the grant is taken to the statement of comprehensive income over the useful life of the non-current asset that has been acquired.

4.11 (a)   The two inventory valuation methods allowed by IAS 2, *Inventories*, are:

- FIFO (first in, first out) assumes that those items bought first are the first to be used in production or selling.

- AVCO (average cost), or weighted average cost method whereby the average cost of items held at the beginning of any period is calculated and, as the inventories are issued for production or selling purposes, all items are issued at that average price. When new inventory is received, the average issue price will then need to be recalculated.

(b)   LIFO (last in, first out) cannot be used under IAS 2.

4.12 at the lower of cost and net realisable value

4.13 IAS 38, *Intangible Assets*, sets out the accounting treatment for expenditure on research and development.

The costs of developing the new lawnmower are likely to be classified, for the purpose of the financial statements, as development costs. Such costs are either recognised as an expense in the statement of comprehensive income when they are incurred, or they may be capitalised (ie recognised on the statement of financial position) as an intangible asset. In order to apply the latter treatment, Lawnderer Limited must be able to demonstrate all of the following criteria given by IAS 38:

- the technical feasibility of completing the intangible asset so that it will be available for use or sale

- its intention to complete the intangible asset and to use or sell it

- its ability to use or sell the intangible asset

- the way in which the intangible asset will generate probable future economic benefits

- the availability of resources to complete the development and to use or sell the intangible asset

- its ability to measure the development expenditure reliably

The project would appear to fulfil all of the criteria, subject to the resource of finance being available either from the company's bank or from shareholders willing to invest more capital.

If all of the criteria are met then the costs of the development may be capitalised and carried on the statement of financial position as an intangible asset until such time as the project commences commercial production. The intangible asset will then be amortised over its useful life against future profits. The effect of this is that the development costs will not affect profits until production commences and sales are made.

5 Chapter activities – answers
Accounting for liabilities and the statement of comprehensive income

5.1 in the statement of comprehensive income and as a current liability in the statement of financial position

5.2 at the lower of the fair value of the asset being leased and the present value of the minimum lease payments

5.3 (a) • A *provision* is a liability of uncertain timing or amount

  • A *contingent liability* is

   – either a possible obligation arising from past events whose existence will be confirmed only by the occurrence or non-occurrence of one or more uncertain future events not wholly within the entity's control

   – or a present obligation that arises from past events but is not recognised because:

    (i) either it is not probable that an outflow of economic benefits will be required to settle the obligation

    (ii) or the obligation cannot be measured with sufficient reliability

  • A contingent asset is a possible asset arising from past events whose existence will be confirmed only by the occurrence or non-occurrence of one or more uncertain future events not wholly within the entity's control.

  (b) • A *provision* is to be recognised as a liability in the financial statements when:

   – an entity has a present obligation as a result of a past event

   – it is probable that an outflow of economic benefits will be required to settle the obligation

   – a reliable estimate can be made of the amount of the obligation

  Note that the word 'probable' used in IAS 37 means that there is a more than 50% likelihood of occurrence of the obligation.

  A provision should also be disclosed as a note to the financial statements, giving:

   – details of changes in the amount of provisions between the beginning and end of the year

   – a description of the provision(s) and expected timings of any resulting transfers

   – an indication of the uncertainties regarding the amount or timing of any resulting transfers

A *contingent liability* is not recognised in the financial statements; however, it should be disclosed as a note to the financial statements which includes:

 – a brief description of the nature of the contingent liability

 – an estimate of its financial effect

 – an indication of the uncertainties relating to the amount or timing of any outflow

 – the possibility of any reimbursement

Note that a contingent liability is a 'possible' obligation, ie a less than 50% likelihood of its occurrence.

Where a contingent liability is considered to be remote, then no disclosure is required in the notes to the financial statements.

A *contingent asset* is not recognised in the financial statements. It is disclosed only where an inflow of economic benefits is probable; disclosure in the notes to the financial statements should include:

 – a brief description of the nature of the contingent asset

 – an estimate of its financial effect

5.4 2 only

5.5 True

5.6 Notes for the directors of Cortez Limited

(a) The fire at the warehouse and the subsequent losses that resulted are a non-adjusting event under IAS 10, *Events after the Reporting Period*. These are events that take place after the financial statements have been prepared at the year end and before the time when the statements are authorised for issue to interested parties. Provision is required in the year end accounts only for adjusting events which are events that provide evidence of conditions that existed at the end of the reporting period. Non-adjusting events should be disclosed if they are of such materiality that non-disclosure would affect the ability of the users of financial statements to reach a proper understanding of the financial position of the company. As this event is disclosed in a note to the accounts it meets these criteria.

(b) The accounting treatment for "deferred tax" is set out in IAS 12, *Income Taxes*. Deferred tax liabilities are amounts of income taxes payable in future periods in respect of taxable temporary differences. These temporary differences arise when the tax due for a particular accounting period is deferred because of the impact of capital allowances or other factors. Deferred tax comes about because the taxable profit of a business is often different from the profit shown in the statement of comprehensive income – for example, capital allowances in excess of depreciation charged in the financial statements may be allowed for tax purposes and result in a saving of corporation tax which later reverses.

IAS 12 requires that deferred tax liabilities should be recognised for all taxable temporary differences (with the exception of goodwill and the initial recognition of certain assets and liabilities). Thus the non-current liability in the statement of financial position arises from timing differences of this sort.

5.7   (a)   IAS 18, *Revenue*, defines revenue as the gross inflow of economic benefits arising from the ordinary activities of an entity.

As well as the sale of goods, other examples of revenue are rendering of services, interest, royalties and dividends.

(b)   Revenue is to be measured at the fair value of the consideration received or receivable.

Fair value is the amount for which an asset could be exchanged, or a liability settled, between knowledgeable, willing parties in an arm's length transaction.

(c)   Revenue from the sale of goods should be recognised when all of the following criteria have been met:

- the seller of the goods has transferred to the buyer the significant risks and rewards of ownership

- the seller retains no continuing managerial involvement in the goods and no effective control over the goods

- the amount of revenue can be measured reliably

- it is probable that the economic benefits will flow to the seller

- the costs incurred, or to be incurred, in respect of the transaction can be measured reliably

5.8   all of them

5.9 **Task 1**

Basic earnings per share

profit for the year attributable to equity holders

$$\frac{\text{Profit after tax*}}{\text{Number of issued ordinary shares}} = \frac{£810,000}{40,000,000} = 2.03\text{p per share}$$

* total comprehensive income for the year

profit for the year from continuing operations attributable to equity holders

$$\frac{\text{Profit after tax from continuing operations}}{\text{Number of issued ordinary shares}} = \frac{£750,000}{40,000,000} = 1.88\text{p per share}$$

Both of these EPS figures are to be presented on the face of the income statement.

Task 2

New issue of shares at full market value

EPS is calculated on the basis of the weighted number of shares in issue during the period. This would be:

40,000,000 + (10,000,000 ÷ 4 [quarter of a year, ie three months]) = 42,500,000

EPS calculation would be:

profit for the year attributable to equity holders

$$\frac{£810,000}{42,500,000} = 1.91\text{p per share}$$

profit for the year from continuing operations attributable to equity holders

$$\frac{£750,000}{42,500,000} = 1.76\text{p per share}$$

5.10 2 and 3

6

Chapter activities – answers
Statement of cash flows

6.1   £45,000 inflow

6.2   £6,000 outflow

6.3   £210,000 inflow

6.4   (a)

Carmen Ltd – Reconciliation of profit from operations to net cash from operating activities	
	£000
Profit from operations	2,200
Adjustments for:	
Depreciation	2,340
Dividends received	(30)
Loss on disposal of property, plant and equipment	50
Decrease/(increase) in inventories	(1,088)
Decrease/(increase) in trade and other receivables	127
(Decrease)/increase in trade and other payables	1,055
Cash generated by operations	4,654
Tax paid	(575)
Interest paid	(190)
Net cash from operating activities	3,889

(b)

Carmen Ltd – Statement of cash flows for year ended 31 March 20X1	
	£000
Net cash from operating activities	3,889
Investing activities	
Dividends received	30
Proceeds on disposal of property, plant and equipment	90
Purchases of property, plant and equipment	(4,080)
Net cash used in investing activities	(3,960)
Financing activities	
Bank loans repaid	(200)
Proceeds of share issue	700
Dividends paid	(1,050)
Net cash from financing activities	(550)
Net increase/(decrease) in cash and cash equivalents	(621)
Cash and cash equivalents at beginning of year	135
Cash and cash equivalents at end of year	(486)

(c)

Carmen Ltd – Statement of changes in equity for the year ended 31 March 20X1

	Share Capital	Other Reserves	Retained Earnings	Total Equity
Balance at 1 April 20X0	10,000	1,000	8,363	19,363
Changes in equity for 20X1				
Profit for the year			1,660	1,660
Dividends			(1,050)	(1,050)
Issue of share capital	500	200		700
Balance at 31 March 20X1	10,500	1,200	8,973	20,673

Tutorial notes:

Proceeds on disposal of property, plant and equipment	*£000*
Cost price	520
– Accumulated depreciation	380
Carrying amount	140
– Loss on disposal	(50)
Proceeds	90

Purchase of property, plant and equipment	
Carrying amount at 1 April 20X0	13,750
– Carrying amount of asset disposal	140
– Depreciation charge for year	2,340
	11,270
+ Purchased during year (missing figure)	4,080
Carrying amount at 31 March 20X1	15,350

Dividends received

In this answer, dividends received have been classified as investing activities. Note that IAS 7, *Statement of Cash Flows*, does permit dividends (and also interest) to be classified as operating or investing or financing activities – how they are classified should be applied consistently in a company's financial statements.

6.5 **Task 1**

UNDERDESK LIMITED

**Reconciliation of profit from operations to net cash from operating activities
for the year ended 31 December 20-7**

	£000
Profit from operations	673
Adjustments for:	
Depreciation	672
Gain on disposal of non-current assets	(29)
Increase in inventories (607–543)	(64)
Increase in trade receivables (481–426)	(55)
Increase in trade payables (371–340)	31
Cash generated by operations	1,228
Interest paid	(156)
Tax paid	(124)
Net cash from operating activities	948

Task 2

UNDERDESK LIMITED

STATEMENT OF CASH FLOWS FOR THE YEAR ENDED 31 DECEMBER 20-7

	£000	£000
Net cash from operating activities		948
Investing activities		
Purchase of non-current assets (see below)	(3,239)	
Proceeds on disposal of non-current assets	114	
Net cash used in investing activities		(3,125)
Financing activities		
Proceeds of share issue (at a premium)	900	
Repayment of share capital	–	
New long-term loans raised	1,180	
Dividends paid	(96)	
Net cash from financing activities		1,984
Net decrease in cash and cash equivalents		(193)
Cash and cash equivalents at beginning of year		104
Cash and cash equivalents at end of year		(89)

Working note

Purchase of non-current assets (*£000*):

Opening balance £2,979 – carrying amount of asset disposal £85 – depreciation £672 + additions
(missing figure) = Closing balance £5,461. Therefore, (missing figure) = £3,239.

Chapter activities – answers
Interpretation of financial statements

7.1

Ratio	(a) Formula	(b) Calculation of ratio (amounts in £000)
(i) Gross profit percentage	$\dfrac{\text{Gross profit}}{\text{Revenue}} \times 100$	$\dfrac{85}{225} \times 100 = 37.8\%$
(ii) Distribution costs/revenue percentage	$\dfrac{\text{Distribution costs} \times 100}{\text{Revenue}}$	$\dfrac{20}{225} \times 100 = 8.9\%$
(iii) Operating profit percentage	$\dfrac{\text{Profit from operations}}{\text{Revenue}} \times 100$	$\dfrac{40}{225} \times 100 = 17.8\%$
(iv) Interest cover	$\dfrac{\text{Profit from operations}}{\text{Finance costs}}$	$\dfrac{40}{10} = 4 \text{ times}$

7.2

Ratio	(a) Formula	(b) Calculation of ratio (amounts in £000)
(i) Current ratio	Current assets Current liabilities	$\dfrac{870}{410}$ = 2.1:1
(ii) Acid test (quick) ratio	Current assets – inventories Current liabilities	$\dfrac{870-380}{410}$ = 1.2:1
(iii) Inventory turnover	Cost of sales Inventories	$\dfrac{3,360}{380}$ = 8.8 times
(iv) Inventory holding period	$\dfrac{\text{Inventories}}{\text{Cost of sales}}$ x 365 days	$\dfrac{380}{3,360}$ x 365 = 41.3 days
(v) Trade receivables collection period	$\dfrac{\text{Trade receivables}}{\text{Revenue}}$ x 365 days	$\dfrac{450}{4,390}$ x 365 = 37.4 days
(vi) Trade payables payment period	$\dfrac{\text{Trade payables}}{\text{Cost of sales}}$ x 365 days	$\dfrac{410}{3,360}$ x 365 = 44.5 days
(vii) Gearing ratio	$\dfrac{\text{Non-current liabilities}}{\text{Total equity + non-current liabilities}}$ x 100	$\dfrac{320}{590+320}$ x 100 = 35.2%

7.3

Ratio	(a) Formula	(b) Calculation of ratio (amounts in £000)
(i) Return on capital employed	$\dfrac{\text{Profit from operations}}{\text{Total equity + non-current liabilities}} \times 100$	$\dfrac{120}{720 + 100} \times 100 = \quad 14.6\%$
(ii) Return on total assets	$\dfrac{\text{Profit from operations}}{\text{Total assets}} \times 100$	$\dfrac{120}{870} \times 100 \quad = \quad 13.8\%$
(iii) Return on equity	$\dfrac{\text{Profit after tax}}{\text{Total equity}} \times 100$	$\dfrac{90}{720} \times 100 \quad = \quad 12.5\%$
(iv) Earnings per share	$\dfrac{\text{Profit after tax}}{\text{Number of issued ordinary shares}}$	$\dfrac{90}{500} \quad\quad = 18 \text{ pence}$
(v) Asset turnover (total assets)	$\dfrac{\text{Revenue}}{\text{Total assets}}$	$\dfrac{1,450}{870} \quad\quad = 1.7 \text{ times}$

7.4

	REPORT		

To:	Managing Director, Bragg Plc	From:	AAT student
Subject:	Interpretation of ratios	Date:	Today

Introduction

This report has been prepared to assist in the interpretation of the financial statements of Roy Limited and Ishiguro Limited, the possible private limited companies in which you are considering the purchase of a majority holding. The report considers the profitability and the financial position of each of the companies for the year ended 31 March 20-4, and compares the results between them.

Calculation of the ratios (amounts in £000)

Ratio	Roy Limited		Ishiguro Limited	
Return on equity	$\dfrac{1,877}{7,367}$	= 25.5%	$\dfrac{1,356}{7,497}$	= 18.1%
Gross profit percentage	$\dfrac{4,751}{8,483}$	= 56.0%	$\dfrac{5,445}{10,471}$	= 52.0%
Gearing ratio	$\dfrac{2,000}{7,367 + 2,000}$	= 21.4%	$\dfrac{6,500}{7,497 + 6,500}$	= 46.4%
Interest cover	$\dfrac{2,630}{160}$	= 16.4 times	$\dfrac{2,304}{520}$	= 4.4 times

Explanation and comment

Return on equity:
- this ratio measures the percentage of profit after tax available for equity shareholders that is generated by the use of equity finance
- the return on equity of Roy Limited is higher than that of Ishiguro Limited
- this means that more profits for equity shareholders are generated from an investment in Roy Limited
- thus an investment in Roy Limited is initially more attractive

Gross profit percentage:
- this ratio shows in percentage terms how much gross profit is being generated by the revenue of the company
- the gross profit percentage of Roy Limited is higher than that of Ishiguro Limited
- this indicates that the underlying business in Roy Limited is more profitable than that in Ishiguro Limited
- thus Roy Limited is relatively more attractive than Ishiguro Limited

Gearing ratio:
- the gearing ratio measures the percentage of non-current liabilities to total equity and non-current liabilities
- the ratio in Ishiguro Limited is higher than that in Roy Limited
- this indicates that Ishiguro Limited is more reliant on debt than is Roy Limited; Ishiguro Limited is a riskier company to invest in than Roy Limited; there is the risk that Ishiguro may not generate sufficient profits to maintain the dividend to ordinary shareholders; it may fail to meet interest payments from profits if there is a downturn in profitability
- the greater risk to ordinary shareholders makes Ishiguro Limited a relatively less attractive investment

Interest cover:
- this ratio shows how many times the company could meet its finance costs out of profit from operations
- Ishiguro Limited has lower interest cover than Roy Limited
- this means that Ishiguro Limited may have more difficulty than Roy Limited in meeting finance costs out of profits; however, there is still a reasonable margin for comfort as Ishiguro can meet the finance costs four times over at the current level of profits
- nevertheless, Roy Limited is still a more attractive investment as the risk of defaulting on finance costs is very low

Conclusion
- The ratios show that Roy Limited is a relatively more attractive investment than Ishiguro Limited
- Roy Limited is the more profitable company with a higher return on equity and higher gross profit percentage
- Roy Limited has a more secure financial position – being lower geared with a much higher interest cover than Ishiguro Limited; this suggests that returns to shareholders from investing in Roy Limited are less risky than those of Ishiguro Limited
- My overall recommendation, on the basis of the ratios calculated and analysis performed, is that Bragg Limited should invest in Roy Limited rather than in Ishiguro Limited

7.5   **(a)**   **Mercia Printers Limited**
            (amounts in £000)

                                                                                        Industry average
Return on capital employed

$$\frac{\text{Profit from operations}}{\text{Total equity + non-current liabilities}} \times 100 \qquad \frac{200}{606 + 250} \times 100 = 23.4\% \qquad 16\%$$

Gearing ratio

$$\frac{\text{Non-current liabilities}}{\text{Total equity + non-current liabilities}} \times 100 \qquad \frac{250}{606 + 250} \times 100 = 29.2\% \qquad 21\%$$

Current ratio

$$\frac{\text{Current assets}}{\text{Current liabilities}} \qquad \frac{580}{174} \times 100 = 3.3{:}1 \qquad 1.8{:}1$$

Operating profit percentage

$$\frac{\text{Profit from operations}}{\text{Revenue}} \times 100 \qquad \frac{200}{2{,}750} \times 100 = 7.3\% \qquad 8\%$$

Trade payables payment period

$$\frac{\text{Trade payables}}{\text{Cost of sales}} \times 365 \qquad \frac{133}{2{,}200} \times 365 = 22.1 \text{ days} \qquad 62 \text{ days}$$

(b)

To.   The Directors

From   AAT student

Date   Today

Report on Mercia Printers Limited performance and efficiency for the year ended 31 August 20-4

The company has appeared to utilise its capital far more profitably than its competitors. Its **return on capital employed** of 23.4% is much better than the industry average of 16%. Therefore, from a profit and investment point of view, the company is very favourably placed.

Gearing is a measure of risk – it reflects the balance between non-current liabilities and total equity plus non-current liabilities. Here the company reports 29.2% against an industry average of 21%. The company has proportionately more money tied up in non-current borrowed funds than is the norm in this industry sector. However 29.2% is still relatively low (a gearing ratio in excess of 50% indicates a high-geared company) and there is the possibility that more funds could be borrowed to finance future growth and expansion.

The **current ratio** measures the short-term day-to-day financing (liquidity) of the business. Here the company has £3.30 of current assets to cover every £1.00 worth of current liabilities. This is a healthy margin, and is proof that the company does not suffer from any cash flow problems. The ratio is well in excess of the industry average of 1.8.

The **operating profit percentage** measures the profitability of the business. The company reports 7.3% against an industry average of 8%, so it is under-performing in this area. The company could look into its pattern of expenditure to see if any economies can be made which would increase profit and bring it back in line with the sector average. Key items of expenditure in this area are wages and salaries and advertising. The company could also look to reducing its cost of sales – reducing the price it pays for paper, for example.

The **trade payables payment period** measures the average amount of time it takes for the company to pay its suppliers. Here it is paying very promptly with a result of 22.1 days against a sector average of 62 days. It might be suggested that the company could benefit its cash by from extending the terms it obtains from suppliers, especially as liquidity is not a problem.

In conclusion, the company performs better than the sector average in three out of the five ratios. The areas which could be investigated are gearing (which, although higher than the industry norm, is still relatively low), and profitability (where the return is below the industry norm by almost 1%).

8 Chapter activities – answers
Consolidated financial statements

8.1   £20,000

8.2   £72,000

8.3   £620,000

8.4   •   *Method of accounting to be used in acquisitions*

The acquisition method is to be used. This measures the cost of assets and liabilities being acquired and usually results in the recognition of goodwill.

•   *Assets and liabilities acquired*

Assets and liabilities being acquired are identified and valued at their fair value on the date of acquisition.

•   *Goodwill*

Goodwill is the excess of the cost of acquisition over the fair value of the identifiable assets and liabilities acquired. Such positive goodwill must be tested for impairment at least annually.

Where the cost of the acquisition is less than the fair value of assets and liabilities acquired, there is negative goodwill. IFRS 3 says that, where negative goodwill is indicated, the first step should be to check the values used to ensure that they are correct. Negative goodwill is recognised in the statement of comprehensive income immediately.

8.5 (a) IFRS 3, *Business Combinations*, requires that the cost of the business acquired is to be measured at the total of:

- the fair values of all the assets and liabilities that existed at the date of acquisition

- any costs directly attributable to the business combination

Fair value is the amount for which an asset could be exchanged between knowledgeable, willing parties in an arm's length transaction (IAS 16, *Property, Plant and Equipment*). For example, the fair value of land and buildings would be the market value, for plant and equipment it would also be the market value, for raw materials it would be the current replacement cost.

The procedure for dealing with fair values is to restate the subsidiary's statement of financial position using fair values. Increases in the valuation of assets are credited to revaluation reserve; decreases are debited to revaluation reserve. Any changes to the value of liabilities are also passed through revaluation reserve. Note that, to be dealt with in this way, the fair value of identifiable assets and liabilities must be capable of being measured reliably.

(b) Fair value has an effect on the calculations for goodwill, non-controlling interest (where applicable), and sometimes on post-acquisition profits:

- goodwill is the excess of the cost of the acquisition over the fair value of the identifiable assets and liabilities acquired

- non-controlling interest is the proportion of the subsidiary owned, based on the fair value of the subsidiary's identifiable assets and liabilities

- post-acquisition profits will be affected where the use of fair value for non-current assets leads to a different depreciation charge from that based on historic costs

8.6 **Task 1**

Shopan Limited: Consolidated statement of financial position as at 30 September 20-9

ASSETS	£000
Non-current assets	
Intangible assets – goodwill	222
Tangible assets	8,306
	8,528
Current assets	
Inventories	2,766
Trade receivables	2,102
Cash and cash equivalents	288
	5,156
Total assets	13,684
EQUITY AND LIABILITIES	
Equity	
Share capital	2,000
Share premium	950
Retained earnings	4,246
Equity attributable to equity holders of the parent	7,196
Non-controlling interest	626
Total equity	7,822
Non-current liabilities	
Long-term loan	3,270
	3,270
Current liabilities	
Trade payables	1,973
Tax liability	619
	2,592
Total liabilities	5,862
Total equity and liabilities	13,684

Workings

1 Shopan Limited holding in Hower Limited

$$\frac{375,000}{500,000} = 75\%$$

Non-controlling interest

$$\frac{125,000}{500,000} = 25\%$$

2   Revaluation of non-current assets in Hower Limited to fair value at date of acquisition:

Debit Non-current assets   £400,000

Credit Revaluation reserve   £400,000

Hence, non-current assets = (6,273,000 + £400,000) + £1,633,000 = £8,306,000

3   Calculation of goodwill arising on consolidation and non-controlling interest:

	Equity	Attributable to Shopan Ltd	Non-controlling Interest
	100%	*75%*	*25%*
All £000			
Share capital	500	375	125
Share premium	120	90	30
Revaluation reserve	400	300	100
Retained earnings	1,484	1,113	371
	2,504	1,878	626
Consideration		2,100	
Goodwill arising on consolidation		222	

Task 2

According to IFRS 3, *Business Combinations*, control is assumed when the acquirer owns more than 50 per cent of the voting shares of the acquiree.

Where there is a less than 50 per cent ownership of voting shares, control can still be obtained if the acquirer has:

- power over more than 50 per cent of the voting rights of the other company as a result of an agreement with other investors
- power to govern the financial and operating policies of the other company as a result of legislation or an agreement
- power to appoint or remove the directors of the other company
- power to cast the majority of votes at a board meeting of the other company

8.7   **Fairway plc and its subsidiary**

Consolidated statement of comprehensive income for the year ended 30 June 20-2

Continuing operations		£000
Revenue	£12,200 + £4,400 – £1,000	15,600
Cost of sales	£8,500 + £3,100 – £1,000	(10,600)
Gross profit		5,000
Distribution costs	£1,600 + £500	(2,100)
Administrative expenses	£400 + 200	(600)
Profit from operations		2,300
Finance costs	£300 + £200	(500)
Profit before tax		1,800
Tax		(500)
Profit for the period from continuing operations		1,300
Attributable to:		
Equity holders of the parent	£1,300 – £60	1,240
Non-controlling interest	20% x £300*	60
		1,300

* Green's after-tax profit for the year

8.8 **(a)**

Perran Ltd – Consolidated statement of financial position as at 31 March 20X1	
	£000
Assets	
Goodwill	78
Non-current assets	1,570
Current assets	730
Total assets	2,378
Equity and liabilities	
Equity	
Share capital	1,000
Retained earnings	498
Non-controlling interest	180
Total equity	1,678
Non-current liabilities	170
Current liabilities	530
Total liabilities	700
Total equity and liabilities	2,378

Tutorial notes:

Goodwill	£
80% x (£600,000 + £240,000)	672,000
Price paid	750,000
Goodwill	78,000

Retained earnings
£450,000 + (80% x [£300,000 – £240,000])

Non-controlling interest
£900,000 x 20%

Inter-company transaction
£70,000 deducted from the current assets of Perran Plc and from the current liabilities of Porth Ltd

(b)

Fistral Plc – Consolidated statement of comprehensive income for the year ended 31 March 20X1.	
	£000
Continuing operations	
Revenue	24,610
Cost of sales	(14,830)
Gross profit	9,780
Other income	–
Distribution costs and administrative expenses	(5,400)
Profit before tax	4,380

Tutorial notes:

Revenue

£18,250,000 + £6,450,000 – £90,000 inter-company revenue = £24,610,000

Cost of sales

£11,800,000 + £3,100,000 – £90,000 inter-company purchases + £20,000 unrealised profit*

= £14,810,000

* unrealised profit is deducted from closing inventories; the effect of this is to increase cost of sales (because closing inventories are deducted in the cost of sales calculation)

Distribution costs and administrative expenses

£3,750,000 + £1,650,000 = £5,400,000

Profit before tax

£3,100,000 + £1,700,000 – £400,000 inter-company dividend – £20,000 unrealised profit

= £4,380,000

Financial statements

Practice assessment 1

Section 1

Task 1.1

You have been asked to help prepare the financial statements of Hanjoy Ltd for the year ended 31 March 20X1. The company's trial balance as at 31 March 20X1 is shown below.

Hanjoy Ltd

Trial balance as at 31 March 20X1

	Debit £000	Credit £000
Share capital		100,000
Revaluation reserve at 1 April 20X0		20,000
Trade and other payables		9,854
Land and buildings – value/cost	125,500	
accumulated depreciation at 1 April 20X0		15,000
Plant and equipment – cost	40,000	
accumulated depreciation at 1 April 20X0		14,400
Trade and other receivables	17,234	
Accruals		256
5% bank loan repayable 20X9		20,000
Cash and cash equivalents	7,901	
Retained earnings		9,280
Interest paid	1,000	
Sales		100,497
Purchases	60,191	
Distribution costs	15,348	
Administrative expenses	11,627	
Inventories at 1 April 20X0	8,486	
Dividends paid	2,000	
	289,287	289,287

Further information:

- The inventories at the close of business on 31 March 20X1 cost £9,107,000.

- Depreciation is to be provided for the year to 31 March 20X1 as follows:

Buildings	2% per annum	Straight line basis
Plant and equipment	20% per annum	Reducing balance basis

Depreciation is apportioned as follows:

	%
Cost of sales	50
Distribution costs	20
Administrative expenses	30

Land, which is non-depreciable, is included in the trial balance at a value of £50,500,000. It is to be revalued at £60,000,000, and this revaluation is to be included in the financial statements for the year ended 31 March 20X1.

*   Trade receivables include a debt of £12,000 which is to be written off.

•   Distribution costs of £35,000 owing at 31 March 20X1 are to be provided for.

•   The corporation tax charge for the year has been calculated as £1,827,000.

•   All of the operations are continuing operations.

(a)   **Draft the statement of comprehensive income for Hanjoy Ltd for the year ended 31 March 20X1. Use the layout shown below.**

(b)   **Draft the statement of financial position for Hanjoy Ltd as at 31 March 20X1. Use the layout shown on the next page.**

Note:

Additional notes and disclosures are not required.

Hanjoy Ltd – Statement of comprehensive income for the year ended 31 March 20X1.	
	£000
Continuing operations	
Revenue	
Cost of sales	
Gross profit	
Distribution costs	
Administrative expenses	
Profit from operations	
Finance costs	
Profit before tax	
Tax	
Profit for the period from continuing operations	
Other comprehensive income for the year	
Total comprehensive income for the year	

(b)

Hanjoy Ltd – Statement of financial position as at 31 March 20X1.	
	£000
ASSETS	
Non-current assets	
Current assets	
Total assets	
EQUITY AND LIABILITIES	
Equity	
Total equity	
Non-current liabilities	
Current liabilities	
Total liabilities	
Total equity and liabilities	

Task 1.2

The directors of Oak plc are reviewing the accounting treatment for their assets under IAS 36 *Impairment of assets.*

Prepare brief notes for the directors of Oak plc to answer the following points:

(a)   **State how, according to IAS 36, an impairment loss is calculated and which two figures are needed.**

(b)   **Explain what is meant by each of these amounts.**

(c)   **State how an impairment loss is to be treated in the financial statements.**

Task 1.3

This task consists of six multiple-choice or true/false questions.

(a)   A decrease in trade receivables will have a negative impact on cash flow in the calculation of net cash flow from operating activities.

✔

True	
False	

(b)   Which one of the following statements best describes the valuation of inventories under IAS 2 *Inventories* at the end of the financial year?

✔

at the lower of FIFO and LIFO	
at the lower of cost and net realisable value	
at the higher of FIFO and AVCO	
at the higher of cost and net realisable value	

(c)   A business prepares its financial statements to 31 December each year. The following events took place after 31 December but before the date on which the financial statements were authorised for issue:

1.   a significant part of the business is to be discontinued

2.   the net realisable value of inventories is found to be materially below the cost price used in the financial statements

Which of the above is likely to be classified as a non-adjusting event under IAS 10, *Events after the Reporting Period*?

✔

1 only	
2 only	
1 and 2	
neither 1 nor 2	

(d) Under IAS 16, *Property, Plant and Equipment*, which of the following costs can be included on initial recognition of property, plant and equipment?

1. cost of testing the asset

2. installation and assembly costs

3. purchase price

4. initial delivery and handling costs

	✔
1 and 2	
2 and 3	
3 and 4	
all of them	

(e) Interest cover is a measure of profitability.

	✔
True	
False	

(f) The issued share capital of Brooker Limited consists of 500,000 ordinary shares of 50 pence each. The reserves of the company currently total £150,000. Huhne plc owns 300,000 ordinary shares in Brooker Limited.

What is the value of the non-controlling interest?

	✔
£160,000	
£240,000	
£400,000	
£500,000	

Task 1.4

Bravo Plc acquired 75% of the issued share capital of Salvo Ltd on 1 April 20X0 for £1,600,000. At that date Salvo Ltd had issued share capital of £1,000,000 and retained earnings of £480,000.

Extracts from the statements of financial position for the two companies one year later at 31 March 20X1 are as follows:

	Bravo Plc £000	Salvo Ltd £000
Assets		
Investment in Salvo Ltd	1,600	
Non-current assets	2,050	1,620
Current assets	1,400	390
Total assets	5,050	2,010
Equity and liabilities		
Equity		
Share capital	2,000	1,000
Retained earnings	1,900	640
Total equity	3,900	1,640
Non-current liabilities	350	220
Current liabilities	800	150
Total liabilities	1,150	370
Total equity and liabilities	5,050	2,010

Additional data

- Included within the current assets of Bravo Plc and in the current liabilities of Salvo Ltd is an inter-company transaction for £50,000 that took place in early March 20X1.
- Bravo Plc has decided non-controlling interest will be valued at their proportionate share of net assets.

(a)   Draft the consolidated statement of financial position for Bravo Plc and its subsidiary undertaking as at 31 March 20X1. Use the layout shown below.

Bravo Ltd – Consolidated statement of financial position as at 31 March 20X1	
	£000
Assets	
Goodwill	
Non-current assets	
Current assets	
Total assets	
Equity and liabilities	
Equity	
Non-controlling interest	
Total equity	
Non-current liabilities	
Current liabilities	
Total liabilities	
Total equity and liabilities	

Weiss Plc acquired 80% of the issued share capital of Hirsh Ltd on 1 April 20X0.

Extracts from their statements of comprehensive income for the year ended 31 March 20X1 are shown below:

	Weiss Plc £000	Hirsh Ltd £000
Continuing operations		
Revenue	30,400	10,300
Cost of sales	(17,800)	(6,100)
Gross profit	12,600	4,200
Other income – dividend from Hirsh Ltd	500	–
Distribution costs and administrative expenses	(4,500)	(1,800)
Profit before tax	8,600	2,400

Additional data

During the year Hirsh Ltd sold goods which had cost £40,000 to Weiss Plc for £100,000. Half of these goods still remain in inventory at the end of the year.

(b)   Draft the consolidated statement of comprehensive income for Weiss Plc and its subsidiary undertaking up to and including the profit before tax line for the year ended 31 March 20X1. Use the layout shown below.

Weiss Plc – Consolidated statement of comprehensive income for the year ended 31 March 20X1.	
	£000
Continuing operations	
Revenue	
Cost of sales	
Gross profit	
Other income	
Distribution costs and administrative expenses	
Profit before tax	

Section 2

Task 2.1

You have been asked to calculate ratios for Nelson Ltd in respect of its financial statements for the year ending 31 March 20X1 to assist your manager in his analysis of the company.

Nelson Ltd's statement of comprehensive income and statement of financial position are set out below.

Nelson Ltd – Statement of comprehensive income for the year ended 31 March 20X1

	20X1 £000
Continuing operations	
Revenue	32,400
Cost of sales	(17,982)
Gross profit	14,418
Distribution costs	(7,319)
Administrative expenses	(4,345)
Profit from operations	2,754
Finance costs	(459)
Profit before tax	2,295
Tax	(531)
Profit for the period from continuing operations	1,764

Nelson Ltd – Statement of financial position as at 31 March 20X1

	20X1 £000
ASSETS	
Non-current assets	
Property, plant and equipment	49,369
Current assets	
Inventories	1,684
Trade receivables	2,833
Cash and cash equivalents	114
	4,631
Total assets	54,000
EQUITY AND LIABILITIES	
Equity	
Share capital	35,000
Retained earnings	15,400
Total equity	50,400
Non-current liabilities	
Bank loans	1,495
	1,495
Current liabilities	
Trade payables	1,574
Tax liability	531
	2,105
Total liabilities	3,600
Total equity and liabilities	54,000

Using the form on the next page:

(a)   State the formulas that are used to calculate each of the following ratios:

    (i)   Gross profit percentage

    (ii)   Operating profit percentage

    (iii)   Return on equity

    (iv)   Current ratio

    (v)   Acid test (quick) ratio

    (vi)   Asset turnover (total assets)

    (vii)   Gearing ratio

    (viii) Interest cover

(b)   Calculate the above ratios (to one decimal place)

Ratio	(a) Formula	(b) Calculation of ratio for Nelson Ltd
(i) Gross profit percentage		
(ii) Operating profit percentage		
(iii) Return on equity		
(iv) Current ratio		
(v) Acid test (quick) ratio		
(vi) Asset turnover (total assets)		
(vii) Gearing ratio		
(viii) Interest cover		

Task 2.2

Steve Horan is a shareholder in Blenheim Ltd and has asked you to assist him in assessing the efficiency and effectiveness of the management of the company. You have calculated the following ratios in respect of Blenheim Ltd's financial statements for the last two years to assist you in your analysis.

	20X1	20X0
Gross profit percentage	42.0%	45.0%
Operating profit percentage	9.5%	7.5%
Inventory holding period	84 days	66 days
Trade receivables collection period	55 days	40 days
Trade payables payment period	50 days	42 days

Prepare a report to Steve that includes:

(a)   A comment on the relative performance of the company for the two years based on the ratios calculated and what this tells you about the company

---

REPORT

To: Steve Horan
From: AAT student
Subject: Shareholding in Blenheim Ltd
Date: Today

---

if required, continue on next page

(b) Advice, with reasons based on the ratios you have calculated, on whether or not Steve
should maintain his investment in the company

Task 2.3

(a) What is the objective of financial statements according to the IASB's *Framework for the Preparation and Presentation of Financial Statements.*

(b) Give TWO examples of external users of financial statements and explain their need for the information in financial statements.

External users	Need for information in financial statements
1.	
2.	

Financial statements

Practice assessment 2

This Assessment is based on a sample assessment provided by the AAT and is reproduced here with their kind permission.

Section 1

Task 1.1

You have been asked to help prepare the financial statements of Pine Ltd for the year ended 31 March 20X1. The company's trial balance as at 31 March 20X1 is shown below.

Pine Ltd

Trial balance as at 31 March 20X1

	Debit	Credit
	£000	*£000*
Share capital		50,000
Revaluation reserve at 1 April 20X0		12,000
Trade and other payables		5,342
Land & buildings – value/cost	81,778	
accumulated depreciation at 1 April 20X0		14,000
Plant and equipment – cost	24,000	
accumulated depreciation at 1 April 20X0		8,000
Trade and other receivables	9,886	
Accruals		517
4% bank loan repayable 20X8		16,000
Cash and cash equivalents	1,568	
Retained earnings		7,945
Interest paid	640	
Sales		80,908
Purchases	53,444	
Distribution costs	9,977	
Administrative expenses	6,755	
Inventories at 1 April 20X0	5,064	
Dividends paid	1,600	
	194,712	194,712

Further information:

■   The inventories at the close of business on 31 March 20X1 cost £7,004,000.

■   Depreciation is to be provided for the year to 31 March 20X1 as follows:

Buildings   5% per annum   Straight line basis

Plant and equipment   25% per annum   Reducing balance basis

Depreciation is apportioned as follows:

	%
Cost of sales	60
Distribution costs	30
Administrative expenses	10

Land, which is non-depreciable, is included in the trial balance at a value of £41,778,000. It is to be revalued at £51,000,000, and this revaluation is to be included in the financial statements for the year ended 31 March 20X1.

■   Trade receivables include a debt of £24,000 which is to be written off.

■   Distribution costs of £160,000 owing at 31 March 20X1 are to be provided for.

■   The corporation tax charge for the year has been calculated as £1,254,000.

■   All of the operations are continuing operations.

(a)   Draft the statement of comprehensive income for Pine Ltd for the year ended 31 March 20X1.

(b)   Draft the statement of financial position for Pine Ltd as at 31 March 20X1.

Note:

Additional notes and disclosures are not required.

Alternative format for Task 1.1

You have been asked to prepare the statement of cash flows and statement of changes in equity for Eigg Ltd for the year ended 31 March 20X1.

The most recent statement of comprehensive income and statement of financial position (with comparatives for the previous year) of Eigg Ltd are set out below.

Eigg Ltd – Statement of comprehensive income for the year ended 31 March 20X1

Continuing operations	£000
Revenue	44,800
Cost of sales	(24,640)
Gross profit	20,160
Dividends received	120
Gain on disposal of property, plant and equipment	448
Distribution costs	(9,408)
Administrative expenses	(4,480)
Profit from operations	6,840
Finance costs	(105)
Profit before tax	6,735
Tax	(2,884)
Profit for the period from continuing operations	3,851

Eigg Ltd – Statement of financial position as at 31 March 20X1

	20X1	20X0
	£000	£000
ASSETS		
Non-current assets		
Property, plant and equipment	27,890	21,340
Current assets		
Inventories	5,914	4,928
Trade and other receivables	4,480	5,376
Cash and cash equivalents	280	0
	10,674	10,304
Total assets	38,564	31,644

EQUITY AND LIABILITIES		
Equity		
Share capital	4,500	3,000
Share premium	3,000	2,000
Retained earnings	24,216	20,642
Total equity	31,716	25,642
Non-current liabilities		
Bank loans	1,500	500
	1,500	500
Current liabilities		
Trade payables	2,464	4,435
Tax liabilities	2,884	887
Bank overdraft	0	180
	5,348	5,502
Total liabilities	6,848	6,002
Total equity and liabilities	38,564	31,644

Further information:

■ The total depreciation charge for the year was £4,458,000.

■ Property, plant and equipment costing £878,000 with accumulated depreciation of £334,000 was sold in the year.

■ All sales and purchases were on credit. Other expenses were paid for in cash.

■ A dividend of £277,000 was paid during the year.

(a) Prepare a reconciliation of profit from operations to net cash from operating activities for Eigg Ltd for the year ended 31 March 20X1.

(b) Prepare the statement of cash flows for Eigg Ltd for the year ended 31 March 20X1.

(c) Draft the statement of changes in equity for Eigg Ltd for the year ended 31 March 20X1.

Task 1.2

Elm Plc will be undertaking some research and development activities in the near future. The directors of Elm Plc understand that such activity may result in the recognition of an intangible asset.

Prepare brief notes for the directors of Elm Plc to answer the following questions:

(a) What is meant by an intangible asset according to IAS 38 *Intangible assets*?

(b) What would Elm Plc have to demonstrate about an intangible asset arising from development activities before it can be recognised as an intangible asset in the financial statements?

Task 1.3

This task consists of 6 true/false / multiple choice type questions.

(a) An increase in inventories will have a negative impact on cash flow in the calculation of net cash flows from operating activities.

True / False

(b) Bovey Ltd holds three distinct types of inventory in its warehouse at the end of its accounting year, which are valued as follows:

Product	FIFO (cost) £	LIFO (cost) £	NRV £
I	11,300	13,400	12,800
II	7,600	4,200	5,900
III	15,200	17,000	18,400
	34,100	34,600	37,100

At what value should inventory be stated in Bovey Ltd's financial statements according to IAS 2 *Inventories*?

	✓
(a) £32,400	
(b) £34,000	
(c) £34,100	
(d) £34,600	

(c) Teign Ltd prepares its financial statements to 30 September each year. The following events took place between 30 September and the date on which the financial statements were authorised for issue.

(I) The company made a major purchase of plant and machinery

(II) A customer who owed the company money at 30 September was declared bankrupt

Which of the above is likely to be classified as an adjusting event (according to IAS 10 *Events after the reporting period*)?

	✓
(a) (I) only	
(b) (II) only	
(c) Both	
(d) Neither of them	

(d) Fowey Ltd has four assets which the directors consider may have become impaired.

	Carrying amount £	Fair value less costs to sell £	Value in use £
I	10,000	12,000	14,000
II	8,000	9,000	5,800
III	7,000	3,800	7,200
IV	9,000	4,300	5,200

Which of the above assets will be impaired according to IAS 36 *Impairment of assets*?

	✓
(a) (I) only	
(b) (II) only	
(c) (III) only	
(d) (IV) only	

(e) Tamar Ltd is being sued by a supplier and will have to pay substantial damages if it loses the case. At its accounting year end lawyers advise the company that it is possible (ie less than a 50% likelihood of occurrence) that it may lose the case.

In accordance with IAS 37 *Provisions, contingent liabilities and contingent assets*, the possible future outflow should be:

	✓
(a) Recognised in the statement of financial position as a provision	
(b) Recognised in the statement of financial position as a contingent liability	
(c) Only disclosed as a note to the financial statements	
(d) Neither recognised in the statement of financial position nor included in the notes	

(f) A lease that transfers substantially all of the risks and rewards of ownership to the lessee is known as:

	✓
(a) A finance lease	
(b) An operating lease	

Task 1.4

Lyd Plc acquired 70% of the issued share capital of Wolf Ltd on 1 April 20X0 for £2,800,000. At that date Wolf Ltd had issued share capital of £2,000,000 and retained earnings of £280,000.

Extracts from the statements of financial position for the two companies one year later at 31 March 20X1 are as follows:

	Lyd Plc	Wolf Ltd
	£000	£000
Assets		
Investment in Wolf Ltd	2,800	
Non-current assets	4,700	1,530
Current assets	2,400	2,090
Total assets	9,900	3,620
Equity and liabilities		
Equity		
Share capital	3,000	2,000
Retained earnings	5,200	540
Total equity	8,200	2,540
Non-current liabilities	600	480
Current liabilities	1,100	600
Total liabilities	1,700	1,080
Total equity and liabilities	9,900	3,620

Additional data:

■   Included within the current assets of Lyd Plc and in the current liabilities of Wolf Ltd is an inter-company transaction for £200,000 that took place in early March 20X1.

■   Lyd Plc has decided non-controlling interest will be valued at their proportionate share of net assets.

(a) Draft the consolidated statement of financial position for Lyd Plc and its subsidiary undertaking as at 31 March 20X1.

Claw Plc acquired 90% of the issued share capital of Deer Ltd on 1 April 20X0.

Extracts from their statements of comprehensive income for the year ended 31 March 20X1 are shown below:

	Claw Plc	Deer Ltd
	£000	£000
Continuing operations		
Revenue	40,800	18,600
Cost of sales	(24,200)	(7,300)
Gross profit	16,600	11,300
Other income – dividend from Deer Ltd	1,800	-
Distribution costs & administrative expenses	(2,500)	(1,600)
Profit before tax	15,900	9,700

Additional data:

During the year Deer Ltd sold goods which had cost £100,000 to Claw Plc for £480,000. Half of these goods still remain in inventory at the end of the year.

(b) Draft the consolidated statement of comprehensive income for Claw Plc and its subsidiary undertaking up to and including the profit before tax line for the year ended 31 March 20X1.

Section 2

Task 2.1

You have been asked to calculate ratios for Brook Ltd in respect of its financial statements for the year ending 31 March 20X1 to assist your manager in his analysis of the company.

Brook Ltd's statement of comprehensive income and statement of financial position are set out below.

Brook Ltd – Statement of comprehensive income for the year ended 31 March 20X1

	20X1
	£000
Continuing operations	
Revenue	24,800
Cost of sales	(12,772)
Gross profit	12,028
Distribution costs	(6,800)
Administrative expenses	(3,244)
Profit from operations	1,984
Finance costs	(372)
Profit before tax	1,612
Tax	(992)
Profit for the period from continuing operations	620

Brook Ltd – Statement of financial position as at 31 March 20X1

	20X1
	£000
ASSETS	
Non-current assets	
Property, plant and equipment	18,200
Current assets	
Inventories	1,260
Trade receivables	2,320
Cash and cash equivalents	1,840
	5,420
Total assets	23,620
EQUITY AND LIABILITIES	
Equity	
Share capital	12,000
Retained earnings	7,212
Total equity	19,212
Non-current liabilities	
Bank loans	2,000
	2,000
Current liabilities	
Trade payables	1,416
Tax liabilities	992
	2,408
Total liabilities	4,408
Total equity and liabilities	23,620

(a) State the formulas that are used to calculate each of the following ratios:

(i) Gross profit percentage

(ii) Operating profit percentage

(iii) Return on capital employed

(iv) Current ratio

(v) Acid test ratio

(vi) Trade receivable collection period (days)

(vii) Inventory holding period (days)

(viii) Gearing ratio

(b) Calculate the above ratios.

Task 2.2

Nancy Charlton is considering buying shares in Limden Ltd and has asked you to assist her in determining the level of profitability and risk of the company. You have computed the following ratios in respect of Limden Ltd's financial statements for the last two years to assist you in your analysis.

	20X1	20X0
Gross profit percentage	46.0%	42.0%
Operating profit percentage	6.5%	8.0%
Return on equity	7.4%	10.8%
Gearing	35.2%	22.4%
Interest cover	2.9 times	7.5 times

Prepare a report to Nancy that includes:

(a) A comment on the relative performance of the company for the two years based on the ratios calculated and what this tells you about the company.

(b) Advice, with reasons based on the ratios you have calculated, on whether or not Nancy should invest.

Task 2.3

(a)   List the elements that appear in financial statements according to the *Framework for the Preparation and Presentation of Financial Statements*.

(b)   Define the elements that appear in the statement of financial position of a company in accordance with the definitions in the *Framework for the Preparation and Presentation of Financial Statements*.

Practice assessment 1
– answers

Section 1

Task 1.1

(a)

Hanjoy Ltd – Statement of comprehensive income for the year ended 31 March 20X1.	
	£000
Continuing operations	
Revenue	100,497
Cost of sales	(62,880)
Gross profit	37,617
Distribution costs	(16,707)
Administrative expenses	(13,625)
Profit from operations	7,285
Finance costs	(1,000)
Profit before tax	6,285
Tax	1,827
Profit for the period from continuing operations	4,458
Other comprehensive income for the year	
Gain on revaluation of the land (60,000 – 50,500)	9,500
Total comprehensive income for the year	13,958

(b)

Hanjoy Ltd – Statement of financial position as at 31 March 20X1.	
	£000
ASSETS	
Non-current assets	
Property, plant and equipment	138,980
Current assets	
Inventories	9,107
Trade and other receivables	17,222
Cash and cash equivalents	7,901
	34,230
Total assets	173,210
EQUITY AND LIABILITIES	
Equity	
Share capital	100,000
Retained earnings	11,738
Revaluation reserve	29,500
Total equity	141,238
Non-current liabilities	
Bank loan	20,000
	20,000
Current liabilities	
Trade and other payables	10,145
Tax liability	1,827
	11,972
Total liabilities	31,972
Total equity and liabilities	173,210

Tutorial notes:

Cost of sales	*£000*
Opening inventories	8,486
+ Purchases	60,191
– Closing inventories	9,107
+ Depreciation	
buildings 2% x £75,000 x 50%	750
plant and equipment	
20% x (£40,000 – £14,400) x 50%	2,560
	62,880

Distribution costs	£000
Trial balance	15,348
+ Accrual	35
+ Depreciation	
buildings 2% x £75,000 x 20%	300
plant and equipment	
20% x (£40,000 – £14,400) x 20%	1,024
	16,707

Administrative expenses	
Trial balance	11,627
+ Irrecoverable (bad) debt	12
+ Depreciation	
buildings 2% x £75,000 x 30%	450
plant and equipment	
20% x (£40,000 – £14,400) x 30%	1,536
	13,625

Non-current assets	
Land and buildings per trial balance	125,500
+ Revaluation of land	9,500
– Accumulated depreciation to 1 April 20X0	15,000
– Depreciation of buildings for year 2% x £75,000	1,500
	118,500
Plant and equipment per trial balance	40,000
– Accumulated depreciation to 1 April 20X0	14,400
	25,600
– Depreciation for year 20% x £25,600	5,120
	20,480
Total non-current assets	138,980

Trade and other receivables	
Trial balance	17,234
– Irrecoverable (bad) debt	12
	17,222

Retained earnings	
Trial balance	9,280
+ Profit for period	4,458
– Dividends paid	2,000
	11,738

Revaluation reserve £000

Trial balance 20,000

Gain on revaluation of land £60,000 – £50,500 9,500

29,500

Trade and other payables

Trial balance 9,854

Trial balance accruals 256

Accrual of distribution costs 35

10,145

Task 1.2

(a)

An impairment loss is the amount by which the carrying amount of an asset exceeds its recoverable amount. The loss is calculated as the difference between the asset's recoverable amount and its carrying amount.

(b)

'Carrying amount' is the amount at which an asset is recognised in the statement of financial position after deducting any accumulated depreciation (amortisation) and accumulated impairment losses.

'Recoverable amount' of an asset is the higher of its fair value, less costs to sell, and its value in use. The latter is the present value of the future cash flows expected to be derived from an asset, including cash from its ultimate disposal.

(c)

The value of the asset is reduced to its recoverable amount in the statement of financial position and the impairment loss is recognised immediately in the statement of comprehensive income (unless it relates to a previously revalued asset, when it is debited to the revaluation surplus within equity).

Task 1.3

(a)   False

(b)   at the lower of cost and net realisable value

(c)   1 only

(d)   all of them

(e)   False

(f)   £160,000

Task 1.4

(a)

Bravo Plc – Consolidated statement of financial position as at 31 March 20X1	
	£000
Assets	
Goodwill	490
Non-current assets	3,670
Current assets	1,740
Total assets	5,900
Equity and liabilities	
Equity	
Share capital	2,000
Retained earnings	2,020
Non-controlling interest	410
Total equity	4,430
Non-current liabilities	570
Current liabilities	900
Total liabilities	1,470
Total equity and liabilities	5,900

Tutorial notes:

Goodwill	£
75% x (£1,000,000 + £480,000)	1,110,000
Price paid	1,600,000
Goodwill	490,000

Retained earnings
£1,900,000 + (75% x [£640,000 – £480,000])

Non-controlling interest
£1,640,000 x 25%

Inter-company transaction
£50,000 deducted from the current assets of Bravo Plc and from the current liabilities of Salvo Ltd

(b)

Weiss Plc – Consolidated statement of comprehensive income for the year ended 31 March 20X1.	
	£000
Continuing operations	
Revenue	40,600
Cost of sales	(23,830)
Gross profit	16,770
Other income	–
Distribution costs and administrative expenses	(6,300)
Profit before tax	10,470

Tutorial notes:

Revenue

£30,400,000 + £10,300,000 – £100,000 inter-company revenue = £40,600,000

Cost of sales

£17,800,000 + £6,100,000 – £100,000 inter-company purchases + £30,000 unrealised profit*

= £23,830,000

* unrealised profit is deducted from closing inventories; the effect of this is to increase cost of sales (because closing inventories are deducted in the cost of sales calculation)

Distribution costs and administrative expenses

£4,500,000 + £1,800,000 = £6,300,000

Profit before tax

£8,600,000 + £2,400,000 – £500,000 inter-company dividend – £30,000 unrealised profit

= £10,470,000

Section 2

Task 2.1

Ratio	(a) Formula	(b) Calculation of ratio for Nelson Ltd
(i) Gross profit percentage	$\dfrac{\text{Gross profit}}{\text{Revenue}}$ x 100	$\dfrac{14{,}418}{32{,}400}$ x 100 = 44.5%
(ii) Operating profit percentage	$\dfrac{\text{Profit from operations}}{\text{Revenue}}$ x 100	$\dfrac{2{,}754}{32{,}400}$ x 100 = 8.5%
(iii) Return on equity	$\dfrac{\text{Profit after tax}}{\text{Total equity}}$ x 100	$\dfrac{1{,}764}{50{,}400}$ x 100 = 3.5%
(iv) Current ratio	$\dfrac{\text{Current assets}}{\text{Current liabilities}}$	$\dfrac{4{,}631}{2{,}105}$ = 2.2:1
(v) Acid test (quick) ratio	$\dfrac{\text{Current assets} - \text{inventories}}{\text{Current liabilities}}$	$\dfrac{4{,}631 - 1{,}684}{2{,}105}$ = 1.4:1
(vi) Asset turnover (total assets)	$\dfrac{\text{Revenue}}{\text{Total assets}}$	$\dfrac{32{,}400}{54{,}000}$ = 0.6:1
(vii) Gearing ratio	$\dfrac{\text{Non-current liabilities}}{\text{Total equity} + \text{non-current liabilities}}$ x 100	$\dfrac{1{,}495}{50{,}400 + 1{,}495}$ = 2.9%
(viii) Interest cover	$\dfrac{\text{Profit from operations}}{\text{Finance costs}}$	$\dfrac{2{,}754}{459}$ = 6 times

Task 2.2

(a)

REPORT

To: Steve Horan
From: AAT student
Subject: Shareholding in Blenheim Ltd
Date: Today

As requested I have looked into the financial situation of Blenheim Ltd

(i)   The **gross profit percentage** has deteriorated.

Less gross profit is being generated by sales/gross profit margin on sales.

Deterioration may be due to decreasing its sales price or increasing the cost of sales or both.

Could have been a change in the product mix.

(ii) The **operating profit percentage** has improved.

More operating profit is being generated from sales – possibly an increase in sales volume.

Either an increase in the sales margins or a decrease in expenses, or both.

As the gross margins have deteriorated, must be the result of a decrease in expenses.

(iii) The **inventory holding period** has deteriorated.

It now takes 18 days more to sell the inventory, on average, than it took the year before.

The increase might be due to slow moving inventory that might indicate possible obsolescence problems.

(iv) The **trade receivables collection period** has deteriorated.

It now takes 15 days more to collect the debts, on average, than it took the year before.

It might be due to old debts which might become bad debts in the future.

(v)   The **trade payables payment period** has deteriorated.

It now takes 8 days more to pay credit suppliers, on average, than it took the year before.

If trade payables are not paid on time they could refuse to supply further goods to the company.

(b)

Steve should be advised to consider selling his shares since only the operating profit percentage has improved. The use of resources needs to be urgently reviewed by management as the periods for inventory, trade receivables and trade payables have all deteriorated.

Before making a final decision he should seek further financial information from the company.

Task 2.3

(a)

> The objective of financial statements according to the IASB's *Framework for the Preparation and Presentation of Financial Statements* is 'to provide information about the financial position, performance and changes in financial position of an entity that is useful to a wide range of users in making economic decisions.'

(b)

External users	Need for information in financial statements
Two from:	
Investors	– to help determine whether to buy, hold or sell shares
	– to assess the ability of the entity to pay dividends
Potential investors	– to help determine whether to buy shares and/or bonds
Lenders	– to see whether their loans and interest will be paid when due
Suppliers and other trade payables	– to determine whether amounts owing to them will be paid
Customers	– to see if the entity will be able to continue to supply its products or services
	– to assess the ability of the entity to meet warranty liabilities, and provision of spare parts
Government and government agencies	– to see the use of resources by the entity, including grants
	– to regulate, to check tax payments, and for statistical purposes
The public	– to assess the contribution of the entity to the economy

Practice assessment 2
– answers

Section 1

Task 1.1

(a) **Pine Ltd - Statement of comprehensive income for the year ended 31 March 20X1**

	£000
Continuing operations	
Revenue	80,908
Cost of sales	(55,104)
Gross profit	25,804
Distribution costs	(11,937)
Administrative expenses	(7,379)
Profit from operations	6,488
Finance costs	(640)
Profit before tax	5,848
Tax	(1,254)
Profit for the period from continuing operations	4,594
Other comprehensive income for the year	
Gain on revaluation of the land (51,000 − 41,778)	9,222
Total comprehensive income for the year	13,816

Task 1.1

(b)   **Pine Ltd – Statement of financial position as at 31 March 20X1**

	£000
ASSETS	
Non-current assets	
Property, plant and equipment	87,000
Current assets	
Inventories	7,004
Trade and other receivables	9,862
Cash and cash equivalents	1,568
	18,434
Total assets	105,434
EQUITY AND LIABILITIES	
Equity	
Share capital	50,000
Retained earnings	10,939
Revaluation reserve	21,222
Total equity	82,161
Non-current liabilities	
Bank loans	16,000
	16,000
Current liabilities	
Trade and other payables	6,019
Tax liability	1,254
	7,273
Total liabilities	23,273
Total equity and liabilities	105,434

Alternative format for Task 1.1

(a)   **Eigg Ltd: Reconciliation of profit from operations to net cash from operating activities**

	£000
Profit from operations	6,840
Adjustments for:	
Depreciation	4,458
Dividends received	(120)
Gain on disposal of property, plant and equipment	(448)
Decrease/(increase) in inventories	(986)
Decrease/(increase) in trade receivables	896
(Decrease)/increase in trade payables	(1,971)
Cash generated by operations	8,669
Tax paid	(887)
Interest paid	(105)
Net cash from operating activities	7,677

(b)   **Eigg Ltd – Statement of cash flows for year ended 31 March 20X1**

	£000
Net cash from operating activities	7,677
Investing activities	
Dividends received	120
Proceeds on disposal of property, plant and equipment	992
Purchases of property, plant and equipment	(11,552)
Net cash used in investing activities	(10,440)
Financing activities	
New bank loans raised	1,000
Proceeds of share issue	2,500
Dividends paid	(277)
Net cash from financing activities	3,223
Net increase/(decrease) in cash and cash equivalents	460
Cash and cash equivalents at beginning of year	(180)
Cash and cash equivalents at end of year	280

(c)   Eigg Ltd – Statement of changes in equity for the year ended 31 March 20X1

	Share Capital	Other Reserves	Retained Earnings	Total Equity
Balance at 1 April 20X0	3,000	2,000	20,642	25,642
Changes in equity for 20X1				
Profit for the year			3,851	3,851
Dividends			(277)	(277)
Issue of share capital	1,500	1,000		2,500
Balance at 31 March 20X1	4,500	3,000	24,216	31,716

Task 1.2

(a)   'An identifiable, non-monetary asset without physical substance' (para 8 of IAS 38)

(b)   Elm plc would have to demonstrate (para 57 of IAS 38):

■   The technical feasibility of completing the intangible asset so that it will be available for use or sale

■   Its intention to complete the intangible asset and use or sell it

■   Its ability to use or sell the intangible asset

■   How the intangible asset will generate future economic benefits

■   The availability of adequate technical, financial and other resources to complete the development and to use or sell the intangible asset

■   Its ability to measure reliably the expenditure attributable to the intangible asset during its development

Task 1.3

(a) True.

(b) (a) IAS 2 permits use of the FIFO and weighted average cost methods of valuing inventory (para 25) but not LIFO. Costs should be measured at the lower of cost and net realisable value. Inventories are written down to net realisable value on an item by item basis, or similar items may be grouped together and a comparison made between the total cost of each group of items and their net realisable value.

Given the above, the valuations of the three distinct types of inventory will therefore be:

Inventory

	£
I	11,300
II	5,900
III	15,200
	32,400

(c) (b) (I) is given in IAS 10 (para 22) as an example of a non-adjusting event.

(II) is given in IAS 10 (para 9) as an example of an adjusting event.

(d) (d) According to IAS 36 (para 8) an asset is impaired when its carrying amount exceeds its recoverable amount, where the recoverable amount of an asset is the higher of its fair value less costs to sell and its value in use (para 6). On this basis only asset (IV) is impaired.

(e) (c) In accordance with IAS 37 this potential outflow is classed as a contingent liability and should therefore be disclosed as a note to the financial statements (paras 27 & 86) as the probability is not remote.

(f) (a) A finance lease transfers substantially all the risks and rewards of ownership to the lessee (IAS 17 para 4).

An operating lease is a lease that is not a finance lease (IAS 17 para 4).

Task 1.4

(a)   **Lyd Plc – Consolidated statement of financial position as at 31 March 20X1**

	£000
Assets	
Goodwill	1,204
Non-current assets	6,230
Current assets	4,290
Total assets	11,724
Equity and liabilities	
Equity	
Share capital	3,000
Retained earnings	5,382
Non-controlling interest	762
Total equity	9,144
Non-current liabilities	1,080
Current liabilities	1,500
Total liabilities	2,580
Total equity and liabilities	11,724

(b)   **Claw Plc – Consolidated statement of comprehensive income for the year ended 31 March 20X1**

	£000
Continuing operations	
Revenue	58,920
Cost of sales	(31,210)
Gross profit	27,710
Other income – dividend from Deer Ltd	-
Distribution costs & administrative expenses	(4,100)
Profit before tax	23,610

Section 2

Task 2.1

(a) and (b)   Formulas and calculation of the ratios

Gross profit percentage

$$\frac{\text{Gross profit}}{\text{Revenue}} \times 100 \qquad \frac{12,028}{24,800} \times 100 \qquad =48.5\%$$

Operating profit percentage

$$\frac{\text{Profit from operations}}{\text{Revenue}} \times 100 \qquad \frac{1,984}{24,800} \times 100 \qquad =8.0\%$$

Return on capital employed

$$\frac{\text{Profit from operations}}{\text{Total equity + Non-current liabilities}} \times 100 \qquad \frac{1,984}{19,212 + 2,000} \times 100 \qquad = 9.4\%$$

Current ratio

$$\frac{\text{Current assets}}{\text{Current liabilities}} \qquad \frac{5,420}{2,408} \qquad = 2.3:1$$

Acid test ratio

$$\frac{\text{Current assets − Inventories}}{\text{Current liabilities}} \qquad \frac{4,160}{2,408} \qquad = 1.7:1$$

Trade receivable collection period (days)

$$\frac{\text{Trade receivables}}{\text{Revenue}} \times 365 \qquad \frac{2,320}{24,800} \times 365 \qquad = 34.1 \text{ days}$$

Inventory holding period (days)

$$\frac{\text{Inventories}}{\text{Cost of sales}} \times 365 \qquad \frac{1,260}{12,772} \times 365 \qquad = 36.0 \text{ days}$$

Gearing ratio

$$\frac{\text{Non-current liabilities}}{\text{Total equity + Non-current liabilities}} \times 100 \qquad \frac{2,000}{19,212 + 2,000} \times 100 \qquad = 9.4\%$$

Task 2.2

Report

To: Nancy Charlton

From: AAT student

Subject: Possible investment in Limden Ltd

Date: 18 June 20X1

As requested I have looked into the financial situation of Limden Ltd.

(a)   Comment on the relative performance of the company for the two years and what this tells you about the company:

    (i)   The **gross profit percentage** has improved.

          More gross profit is being generated by sales/gross profit margin on sales.

          Improvement may be due to increasing its sales price or decreasing the cost of sales or both.

          Could have been a change in the product mix.

    (ii)   The **operating profit percentage** has deteriorated.

          Less operating profit is being generated from sales.

          Either a decrease in the sales margins or an increase in expenses, or both.

          As the gross margins have improved, must be the result of an increase in expenses.

    (iii)   The **return on equity** has deteriorated.

          Less net profit is being generated from equity.

    (iv)   The **gearing ratio** has deteriorated.

          Could cause problems obtaining loans in the future.

          More risky.

          May have taken out additional loans during the year

    (v)   The **interest cover ratio** has deteriorated.

          Less operating profit to cover interest payments.

          More risky.

          Caused by lower operating profits/higher interest payments.

          Higher interest payments could be due to new loans taken out during the year.

(b)   A conclusion advising Nancy whether or not to invest:

Nancy should be advised **not to invest** since **only the gross profit percentage has improved** whilst **overall profitability has deteriorated** and any investment would be **risky**.

Task 2.3

(a)   Income

       Expenses

       Assets

       Liabilities

       Equity

(b)   (i)   'An asset is a resource controlled by an entity as a result of past events and from which future economic benefits are expected to flow to the entity.'

       (ii)   'A liability is a present obligation of the entity arising from past events, the settlement of which is expected to result in the outflow from the entity of resources embodying economic benefits.'

       (iii)   'Equity is the residual interest in the assets of the entity after deducting all its liabilities.'